Process Monitoring and Improvement Handbook

Also available from ASQ Quality Press:

Business Process Improvement Toolbox, Second Edition
Bjørn Andersen

Human Error Reduction in Manufacturing
José Rodríguez-Pérez

Handbook of Investigation and Effective CAPA Systems, Second Edition
José Rodríguez-Pérez

*The FDA and Worldwide Current Good Manufacturing Practices and Quality
System Requirements Guidebook for Finished Pharmaceuticals*
José Rodríguez-Pérez

*Quality Experience Telemetry: How to Effectively Use Telemetry for Improved
Customer Success*
Alka Jarvis, Luis Morales, and Johnson Jose

*The ISO 9001:2015 Implementation Handbook: Using the Process Approach to
Build a Quality Management System*
Milton P. Dentch

The Certified Six Sigma Yellow Belt Handbook
Govindarajan Ramu

The Certified Pharmaceutical GMP Professional Handbook, Second Edition
FDC Division and Mark Allen Durivage, editor

*Failure Mode and Effect Analysis: FMEA from Theory to Execution,
Second Edition*
D. H. Stamatis

*The Art of Integrating Strategic Planning, Process Metrics, Risk Mitigation,
and Auditing*
J. B. Smith

*Advanced Quality Auditing: An Auditor's Review of Risk Management, Lean
Improvement, and Data Analysis*
Lance B. Coleman

To request a complimentary catalog of ASQ Quality Press publications,
call 800-248-1946, or visit our website at http://www.asq.org/quality-press.

Process Monitoring and Improvement Handbook

SECOND EDITION

Manuel E. Peña-Rodríguez

ASQ Quality Press
Milwaukee, Wisconsin

American Society for Quality, Quality Press, Milwaukee 53203
© 2019 by ASQ. Printed in 2018
All rights reserved.
Printed in the United States of America
23 22 21 20 19 18   5 4 3 2 1

Library of Congress Cataloging-in-Publication Data

Names: Pena-Rodriguez, Manuel E., author.
Title: Process monitoring and improvement handbook / Manuel E. Pena-Rodriguez.
Description: Second edition. I Milwaukee, Wisconsin : ASQ Quality Press, [2018] I
    Includes bibliographical references and index.
Identifiers: LCCN 2018029361 I ISBN 9780873899741 (hardcover : acid-free paper)
Subjects: LCSH: Process control—Handbooks, manuals, etc. I Quality control—
    Handbooks, manuals, etc.
Classification: LCC TS156.8 .P447 2018 I DDC 660/.2815—dc23
LC record available at https://lccn.loc.gov/2018029361

Director, Quality Press and Programs: Ray Zielke
Managing Editor: Paul Daniel O'Mara
Sr. Creative Services Specialist: Randy L. Benson

ASQ Mission: The American Society for Quality advances individual, organizational,
and community excellence worldwide through learning, quality improvement, and
knowledge exchange.

Attention Bookstores, Wholesalers, Schools, and Corporations: ASQ Quality Press
books, video, audio, and software are available at quantity discounts with bulk
purchases for business, educational, or instructional use. For information, please
contact ASQ Quality Press at 800-248-1946, or write to ASQ Quality Press,
P.O. Box 3005, Milwaukee, WI 53201–3005.

To place orders or to request a free copy of the ASQ Quality Press Publications Catalog,
visit our website at http://www.asq.org/quality-press.

 Printed on acid-free paper

 Quality Press
600 N. Plankinton Ave.
Milwaukee, WI 53203-2914
E-mail: authors@asq.org
ASQ   The Global Voice of Quality™

*To my beloved wife Marisol and my daughter Stacey **Marie**. Thanks for always being by my side, inspiring me in everything I do.*

Also, to my best friend José (Pepe) Rodríguez-Pérez. Thanks for all your support and for letting me travel around the world spreading our passion for quality.

Finally, to all the readers of the first edition who shared with me their wonderful comments. I hope this second edition also fulfills your expectations.

Table of Contents

List of Figures and Tables

Preface

The title of this second edition reveals the importance of process monitoring and improvement in any organization. The first edition focused mainly on statistical process control in industries regulated by the Food and Drug Administration (FDA). However, the concept of process monitoring and improvement applies to any type of industry: automotives, textiles, food, pharmaceuticals, biologics, medical devices, electronics, aerospace, banking, educational institutions, service providers, and so on.

The focus of this book is to identify and apply different process monitoring and improvement tools in any organization. The book is not intended to provide an intensive course in statistics; instead, it is a how-to guide about the application of the diverse array of tools available to monitor and improve processes. This book is aimed at engineers, scientists, analysts, technicians, managers, supervisors, and all other professionals responsible to measure and improve the quality of their processes. Many times, these professionals do not have a formal education on the use of these tools but learn about them throughout the different improvement projects in which they are involved in their work environment. This book is intended to fill the gap between the lack of formal education in the tools and the need to implement those tools in an improvement project. Also, the book is intended to be a refresher course for those professionals who have learned about these tools as part of their educational background.

The book contains 12 chapters and three appendixes. Chapter 1 has been enhanced to explain the importance of process monitoring and improvement in any organization. The requirements for process monitoring and improvement in some International Organization for Standardization (ISO) standards and FDA regulations are presented. Chapter 2 is a completely new chapter that explains different process monitoring approaches and when to use them. Approaches for incoming inspection, in-process inspection, and final inspection are explained in detail. Also, different approaches for incoming inspection are presented in order to reduce sample size systematically as incoming quality gets better.

Then, Chapter 3 presents the concept of *process variation*. The common causes and special causes of variation are explained in detail. Chapter 4 presents some basic statistical concepts, such as types of data, sample collection and sample size calculation, descriptive statistics, the normal distribution, and so on. Next, Chapter 5 presents some of the most useful graphical tools with which to start analyzing processes. Tools such as the histogram, dot plot, box plot, Pareto diagram, scatter plot, and run charts are presented in this chapter, along with examples to show their application.

In Chapter 6, one of the most important but less frequently used tools is presented: the measurement systems analysis. The importance of addressing measurement system variability prior to implementing any other improvement initiative is thoroughly explored in this chapter, which includes an enhanced example of the use of the gage repeatability and reproducibility (R&R) tool before and after an improvement project. Chapter 7 presents the concept of *process capability*. Here, we study the different indices used to measure capability: C_p, C_{pk}, P_p, and P_{pk}. Then, in Chapter 8, an introduction to *hypothesis testing* is presented. Several tools used to compare means, medians, and variances are introduced for normal and nonnormal data. Many examples are provided detailing the use of these tools.

Chapter 9 explains how to use regression analysis to understand the relationship between input variables and output variables. Then, Chapter 10 provides a very brief introduction to *design of experiments*. The concepts of *full factorial* and *fractional factorial* experiments are introduced in this chapter, along with a very simple example of a full factorial experiment and how to interpret the results of that experiment. In Chapter 11, control charts are introduced as a tool to facilitate process monitoring and control. The control charts for variable data and attribute data are presented, along with some applications. Finally, Chapter 12 presents a summary about the recommended order to use the tools presented in the book to monitor and improve processes. Also, the concept of being proactive or reactive in the use of the monitoring and improvement tools is explained with an example.

To visualize the difference between attribute and variable data, Appendix A shows some different tools for analyzing attribute or variable data, including control charts, probability distributions, sampling plans, and measurement instruments for each type of data. Appendix B presents many graphical and statistical tools to be used for different situations, with a reference to the section in the book in which the tool can be found. Finally, Appendix C shows some of the most commonly used hypothesis tests in an easy-to-understand tabular format.

By means of this book, I expect readers can obtain a better understanding of some of the tools available to monitor and improve their processes. Also, I encourage readers to study, with a greater level of detail, each of the tools presented. The content of this book is the result of almost 25 years of experience in the application of monitoring and improvement tools in various industries and the combination of my engineering and legal educational backgrounds, specifically through providing consulting services to hundreds of organizations worldwide.

1

Importance of Process Monitoring and Improvement

1.1 PROCESS MONITORING AND IMPROVEMENT WITHIN THE ISO STANDARDS

A quality management system is a collection of business processes focused on consistently meeting customer requirements and enhancing their satisfaction. It is aligned with an organization's purpose and strategic direction. Process monitoring and improvement are essential requirements of any quality management system. The ISO 9001:2015 standard establishes that the adoption of a quality management system is a strategic decision for an organization that can help to improve its overall performance and provide a sound basis for sustainable development initiatives.[1]

Section 9.1 of the ISO 9001:2015 standard states that, as part of their quality management system, organizations shall determine:

a) What needs to be monitored and measured
b) The methods for monitoring, measurement, analysis, and evaluation needed to ensure valid results
c) When the monitoring and measuring shall be performed
d) When the results from monitoring and measurement shall be analyzed and evaluated[2]

Finally, section 10.1 of ISO 9001:2015 establishes that organizations shall determine and select opportunities for improvement and implement any necessary actions to meet customer requirements and enhance customer satisfaction. These actions shall include:

a) Improving products and services to meet requirements as well as to address future needs and expectations
b) Correcting, preventing, or reducing undesired effects

c) Improving the performance and effectiveness of the quality management system[3]

A good example of process monitoring and improvement requirements as part of the quality management system for a specific sector can be observed in the standard for medical devices, the ISO 13485:2016. For example, section 8.2.5 of the standard requires that organizations shall apply suitable methods for monitoring and, as appropriate, measuring the quality management system processes. These methods shall demonstrate the ability of the processes to achieve planned results. When planned results are not achieved, correction and corrective action shall be taken, as appropriate.[4] Also, section 8.2.6 of the ISO 13485:2016 standard establishes that organizations shall monitor and measure the characteristics of the product to verify that product requirements have been met. This shall be carried out at applicable stages of the product realization process in accordance with the planned and documented arrangements and documented procedures.[5]

Then, section 8.5.1 establishes that organizations shall identify and implement any changes necessary to ensure and maintain the continued suitability, adequacy, and effectiveness of the quality management system as well as medical device safety and performance through the use of the quality policy, quality objectives, audit results, post-market surveillance, analysis of data, corrective actions, preventive actions, and management review.[6]

1.2 PROCESS MONITORING AND IMPROVEMENT WITHIN THE CODE OF FEDERAL REGULATIONS

Several sections within Title 21 of the Code of Federal Regulations (CFR) mention the concept of process monitoring and improvement. I will focus the discussion on two specific sections of Title 21: the section related to finished pharmaceutical products[7] and the section related to medical devices.[8]

It is important to understand that regulations are not intended to provide a specific way to achieve process controls. Regulations provide the *minimum* requirements. For instance, the regulation for finished pharmaceutical products states that regulations in this part contain the minimum current good manufacturing practice for preparation of drug products for administration to humans or animals.[9] The regulation for medical devices establishes the basic requirements applicable to manufacturers of finished medical devices.[10]

Both regulations explicitly state that requirements established therein are the minimum that the manufacturer must accomplish; they are not intended to be a "one size fits all" type of requirement. Let us start with the process controls within the regulation for finished pharmaceutical products.

1.2.1 Current Good Manufacturing Practices (21 CFR 211)

Published in 1978, the current Good Manufacturing Practices (cGMP) provide a framework to control finished pharmaceutical processes. Control over the processes is important so that the product meets standards of safety, efficacy, purity, and stability. Section 211.22 establishes the responsibilities of the *quality control unit* (QCU). This section states that:

> There shall be a quality control unit that shall have the responsibility and authority to approve or reject all components, drug product containers, closures, in-process materials, packaging material, labeling, and drug products, and the authority to review production records to assure that no errors have occurred or, if errors have occurred, that they have been fully investigated. The quality control unit shall be responsible for approving or rejecting drug products manufactured, processed, packed, or held under contract by another company.[11]

To comply with the regulation, the manufacturer shall establish written procedures, which shall be followed. It should be noted that the QCU must establish all process controls, monitor those process controls, and take actions whenever those process controls are not followed. In other words, the QCU is responsible for establishing process monitoring and improvement tools to ensure the quality of pharmaceutical products.

1.2.2 Quality System Regulation (21 CFR 820)

Published in 1996, the current Quality System Regulation (QSR) provides a framework to control medical device processes. Section 820.70 establishes that manufacturers shall develop, conduct, control, and monitor production processes to ensure that a device conforms to its specifications. Where deviations from device specifications could occur as a result of the manufacturing process, the manufacturer shall establish and maintain process control procedures that describe any process controls necessary to ensure conformance to specifications.[12]

Section 820.100 requires that manufacturers shall establish and maintain procedures for implementing corrective and preventive action. The procedures shall include requirements for analyzing processes, work operations, concessions, quality audit reports, quality records, service records, complaints, returned product, and other sources of quality data to identify existing and potential causes of nonconforming product or other quality problems. An appropriate statistical methodology shall be employed where necessary to detect recurring quality problems.[13]

Finally, section 820.250 of the regulation for medical devices explicitly establishes the use of statistical techniques for process monitoring and improvement.[14] It does not prescribe any specific statistical tool or technique but establishes that the technique used must be "valid." Also, the regulation establishes that sampling must have a "valid statistical rationale." In both cases, "valid" means that the tools used must be acceptable, reasonable, and appropriate to the situation at hand. So, the right tool must be used for each situation. That is basically one of the goals of this book: to allow the reader to identify which of the available statistical tools and techniques is the most appropriate for each situation in order to monitor and improve the processes.

1.3 SUMMARY

The ISO standards and the regulations for finished pharmaceutical products and medical devices establish the need to monitor and improve the processes. The tools presented in this book will assist organizations in monitoring processes on a continuous basis to improve their performance. The next chapter presents various sampling and monitoring approaches for different stages of the process.

NOTES

1. International Organization for Standardization, ISO 9001:2015, *Quality management systems—Requirements*, Sec. 0.1—General.
2. ISO 9001:2015, Sec. 9.1—Monitoring, measurement, analysis and evaluation.
3. ISO 9001:2015, Sec. 10.1—Improvement.
4. International Organization for Standardization, ISO 13485:2003, *Medical devices—Quality management systems—Requirements for regulatory purposes*, Sec. 8.2.5—Monitoring and measurement of processes.
5. ISO 13485:2003, Sec. 8.2.6—Monitoring and measurement of processes.
6. ISO 13485:2003, Sec. 8.5.1—Improvement—General.
7. Food and Drug Administration (FDA) 21 Code of Federal Regulations (CFR) Part 211, *Current good manufacturing practices for finished pharmaceuticals* (1978), http://www.ecfr.gov.

8. FDA 21 CFR Part 820, Medical devices: *Current good manufacturing (CGMP) final rule: Quality system regulations* (1996), http://www.ecfr.gov.
9. 21 CFR § 211.1—Scope.
10. 21 CFR § 820.1—Scope.
11. 21 CFR § 211.22—Responsibilities of quality control unit.
12. 21 CFR § 820.70—Production and process controls.
13. 21 CFR § 820.100—Corrective and preventive action.
14. 21 CFR § 820.250—Statistical techniques.

2

Different Approaches for Process Monitoring and When to Use Them

2.1 OVERVIEW

Determining the sample of product is an important consideration for most organizations when they are trying to distinguish between good and defective product. There are different sampling approaches for the inspection stages: incoming, in-process, and final inspections. By implementing these approaches, organizations can improve their inspection activities and provide better product to the customer.[1]

2.2 REPRESENTATIVE SAMPLES

Sampling is one of the most-used methods in quality systems to control the output of any given process. Specifically, sampling allows organizations to distinguish between good product and defective product. In this way, defective product is rejected while good product continues through the production stream. One of the most-discussed topics in sampling is sample size. There are many methods used to determine the size of the sample. One of these methods will be discussed in Chapter 4.

There is, however, another important aspect of sample selection: representativeness of the samples. To be representative, a sample must have the same chance of being collected as the other samples do. Suppose, for example, that a sample size is calculated as 32. Obtaining a representative sample would mean randomly collecting four samples every hour during an eight-hour shift. On the other side, a nonrepresentative sample would be obtained if you collected the first 32 samples of the shift or the last 32 samples of the shift. Using the first approach (four samples every hour), it would be easier to detect defects if they occur randomly throughout the shift. Sampling only at the beginning or end of the shift, however, makes it difficult to detect defects if they happen randomly throughout the shift.

An example would be sampling labels in a continuous roll of paper. If an organization just takes a sample either at the beginning of the roll or at the end of the roll (or both), how would it be possible to detect defects somewhere in the middle of the roll? Even adding a sample in the middle of the roll might not be enough. What will happen if, at three-quarters of the roll, there is a power failure that causes the printer to lose the programming? If you wait until the next sample at the end of the roll, it would be too late. For that reason, another sample should be collected after any planned (or unplanned) interruption of the process.

2.3 SAMPLING VERSUS STATISTICAL PROCESS CONTROL

Sampling is an easy and cost-effective way to monitor a process. The main disadvantage of sampling is that it does not provide much information about the quality level of the process. It only provides binary information: good product or defective product. It does not tell you how good the product is or how bad the defective product is. Based on the traditional concept of variation explained in Genichi Taguchi's loss function[2] (see Figure 2.1), most organizations measure their product quality against specification limits. If the process is within the upper and lower specification limits, the process is assumed to be good and nothing else is done (left side of Figure 2.1).

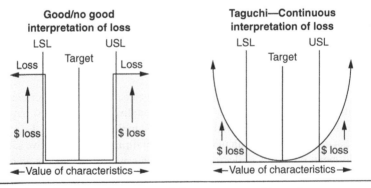

Figure 2.1 Concepts of process variation as compared to customer specifications.

But Taguchi explained that this is not a good approach. Losses start to develop as soon as you deviate from the target value (right side of Figure 2.1). Taguchi calculated the losses using the formula:

$$L = k(y - T)^2$$

in which L is the monetary loss, k is a cost factor, y is the actual value, and T is the target value. Based on Taguchi's loss function, if you want to reduce the losses, you must focus on variation—specifically, on reducing process variation. From the formula, it means that the output value (y) must be as close as possible to the target value (T). As noted previously, sampling does not tell you about the variation of the process. It only allows you to determine whether the product is accepted (good product) or rejected (defective product). So, if you want to learn about process variation, you should not rely only on acceptance sampling. You must have a more dynamic approach. A good method is statistical process control (SPC) using the control chart. This tool will be covered in Chapter 11.

A well-known assumption is that all processes are subject to some kind of variation. The two main types of variation are common-cause variation and special-cause variation:

- *Common-cause variation* is present in every process because no process is perfect. It is inherent in every process.

- *Special-cause variation* is not present in every process and is caused by assignable events; that is, by certain things that have a significant impact on the process.

In a control chart, the control limits define where the common causes of variation are expected to lie. In other words, as long as the process is in statistical control, all the points will lie within the control limits defined by the interval of ±3 sigma from the mean, without any nonrandom pattern. When you see a point outside of those control limits (or points showing a nonrandom pattern), it indicates some sort of assignable or special cause that must be studied and corrected.

A control chart not only allows you to see how the process centering and variation behave on a time-based scale, but it also allows you to see the result of some process improvements. Figure 2.2 shows an example of a control chart in which process improvements have been implemented. Note that because the control limits are calculated based on the process variation, when variation decreases, the control limits must be recalculated to reflect the new, lower variation.

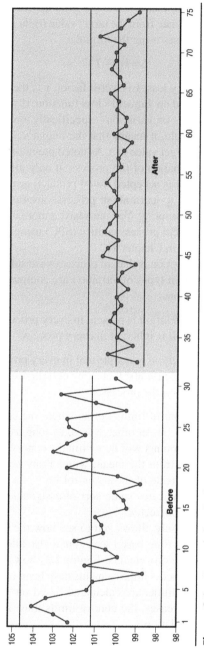

Figure 2.2 Control chart before and after improvements.

2.4 RECOMMENDED APPROACHES AT VARIOUS STAGES

Now that you know some of the advantages and disadvantages of sampling and SPC control charts, let us explore when it is convenient to use sampling and when it is convenient to use control charts to monitor the quality of the process. Let us divide the inspection location into three areas: incoming, in-process, and final.

2.4.1 Incoming Inspection

At this part of the process, the organization is receiving raw materials, packaging materials, purchased components, and so on. It is important to measure the quality of the materials at this stage to avoid accepting defective product that will cause problems downstream. But what is the best approach at this stage of the process? As noted earlier, acceptance sampling is an easy and cost-effective way to assess the quality of the incoming product. Acceptance sampling plans—such as the ANSI/ASQ Z1.4 (for attribute data)[3] and ANSI/ASQ Z1.9 (for variable data)[4]—are common approaches at this stage.

The main disadvantage of these acceptance sampling plans is that, depending on the acceptance quality limit (AQL) values selected, you could have a plan that will accept the entire lot even with one or more defective parts. But this is not a major constraint at this stage. Why? Because the processes must have enough controls to detect all those defective parts that were not detected during the incoming inspection process and reject them during the subsequent process steps. These acceptance sampling plans are designed to provide a high probability of acceptance if the percentage defective is at or below the established AQL. In other words, these plans provide a safeguard to the supplier of the incoming material because you would be still accepting the lot even with a small number of defects.

2.4.2 In-Process Inspection

There are many approaches that organizations use to inspect product while the process is going on. For example, many organizations use acceptance sampling plans, such as the ANSI/ASQ Z1.4 or ANSI/ASQ Z1.9 already mentioned. Other organizations develop some sort of sampling and establish alert limits and action limits to determine the course of action after the sample is collected.

The main problem with these approaches is that the decision is still pass/fail (i.e., continue the process or stop the process and make some adjustments). Typically, the reaction is too late. Another disadvantage of this type of approach is that it does not have memory; that is, each day's decision is taken, but it is registered only on that day's documentation. In this case, because the data are not recorded in a time-based scale, there is no way to see any potential trend. A solution to this dilemma is to record the data and plot it in a control chart.

For example, an organization might be sampling parts at a specific station using the alert limit/action limit approach. At the end of the day, if nothing out of the action limit happens, the organization just archives the form containing the number of defects for that day. If there is an out-of-the-action-limit event, the organization adjusts the process, records the amount of defects, and also archives the form. However, nothing else happens. The recommendation to this organization is to plot the number of defects each day (or each shift, preferably) in a c-control chart, which is a control chart for number of defects that will be explained in Chapter 11.

After enough data (at least a month's worth) have been collected, the organization should calculate the control limits. From that point, it can use the control chart to evaluate the process and determine when an assignable cause has been identified. The control chart is a monitoring tool that can feed other statistical tools to improve processes. If control charts show that shift-to-shift variation is too high, for example, other tools can be used to determine the source of such variability, such as the *F*-test, Levene test, or design of experiments. Some of these tools will be discussed in subsequent chapters. After the improvements are implemented, control charts can be used to track the improvement, as shown in Figure 2.2.

2.4.3 Final Inspection

If all previous inspections (incoming and in-process) are well-executed, there should not be too many defects left from the process after it is completed. Figure 2.3 shows how defects should be funneled throughout the different inspection points. Still, a final inspection is necessary as a warranty that no defective product is released to the customer.

A common approach used by organizations at this stage is to implement the same acceptance sampling plans they used at incoming inspection: ANSI/ASQ Z1.4 or ANSI/ASQ Z1.9. However, as mentioned already, there is a big disadvantage when using this kind of approach: accepting a lot with one or more defects.

To avoid this situation, many organizations start tweaking the inspection plans to obtain a plan with acceptance of zero defective product and

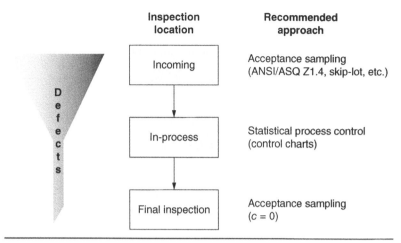

Inspection location	Recommended approach
Incoming	Acceptance sampling (ANSI/ASQ Z1.4, skip-lot, etc.)
In-process	Statistical process control (control charts)
Final inspection	Acceptance sampling ($c = 0$)

Figure 2.3   Approaches to monitor the process.

rejection of one or more defective products. Most of the time, they achieve that plan by selecting a lower AQL. Not only is this an incorrect application of the sampling plan, but the sampling sizes obtained by these plans also are unnecessarily high.

An alternative is to use the zero-acceptance number ($c = 0$) sampling plan developed by Nicholas L. Squeglia.[5] This plan is an adaptation of the acceptance sampling plans covered earlier (specifically, ANSI/ASQ Z1.4). In the zero-acceptance number sampling plan, however, the probability of accepting a lot with a certain percentage of defective product or higher is very low. In this case, there is a safeguard to the customers that no defective product will be released. This safeguard to the customer is not the only reason to use this type of plan at final inspection. Most of the time, the sample sizes calculated from the zero-acceptance number sampling plans are much lower than those for the ANSI/ASQ Z1.4 and at the same AQL values. In other words, the sample sizes will be much lower while keeping the same protection to the customer.

Table 2.1 shows an example of a sampling plan for a lot size of 12,000 parts and an AQL of 0.65. Using the ANSI/ASQ Z1.4, a total of 315 samples would have to be collected, whereas by using the $c = 0$ sampling plan, only 77 samples would have to be collected (a 76% reduction). Not only is there a significant reduction in the sample size, but for the ANSI/ASQ Z1.4 plan, the lot could still be accepted with five defective parts and rejected with six defective parts. If zero defective parts is the only accepted level, the AQL must be reduced to 0.040. As noted earlier, reducing the AQL is not the right approach.

Table 2.1 Example of a sampling plan using ANSI/ASQ Z1.4 and c = 0 plans.

	ANSI/ASQ Z1.4	**c = 0**
Lot size	12,000	12,000
Inspection level	II	N/A
AQL	0.65	0.65
Sample size	315	77
Accept (Ac)	5*	0
Reject (Re)	6*	1

*If an Ac = 0 and Re = 1 is desired, then an AQL of 0.040 (instead of 0.65) would be required

It is important to note another aspect of the c = 0 sampling plan: When one or more defective products are obtained using this plan, the lot is withheld. The phrase "withhold the lot" is significant because it does not necessarily mean rejection. Under these plans, the inspector does not necessarily reject the lot if one or more defective products is found. The inspector only accepts the lot if zero defective product is found in the sample. Withholding the lot forces a review and disposition by engineering or management personnel to determine the extent and seriousness of the defective product.

2.5 OTHER SAMPLING APPROACHES FOR INCOMING INSPECTION

In section 2.4, which covered different approaches for process monitoring at different stages, I mentioned that at incoming inspection we can be more flexible than during the other stages, because those defects that could escape the incoming inspection will hopefully be detected throughout the process. Usually, at incoming inspection, acceptance sampling plans (such as ANSI/ASQ Z1.4 for attributes and ANSI/ASQ Z1.9 for variables) are implemented in order to distinguish good lots from defective lots. Let us focus on the acceptance sampling plans for attributes.

One of the most important aspects of ANSI/ASQ Z1.4 is the use of the "switching rules" as the quality of the inspected product improves (or gets worse). There are different inspection schemes used with the switching rules: normal inspection, reduced inspection, and tightened inspection. With some exceptions, the sample size in each of these inspection schemes remains the same after the switch; the only thing that changes from scheme to scheme is the acceptance number. For example, when compared to the normal inspection, the tightened inspection has lower acceptance numbers with the same sample size. On the other hand, reduced inspection has lower sample size as long as the defectives are kept at or below the acceptance number. If the defectives are higher than the acceptance number but lower than the rejection number, normal inspection is reinstated. In this case, the sample size will increase to the size specified for the normal inspection. So, how could we really reduce the sample size as quality gets better?

Table 2.2 shows the sampling amount when using different approaches. For example, when 100% inspection is performed, all parts from all lots are inspected. This seems unrealistic, especially if the sampling is destructive. Even if sampling is not destructive, unless the inspection is 100% automatic, this approach does not seem economically feasible. One of the most widely used inspection approaches for attributes is ANSI/ASQ Z1.4. When this approach is used, all lots are inspected; however, only some parts of each lot are inspected depending on the sampling scheme selected. The sample scheme is defined in terms of lot size, inspection level, and acceptance quality limit (AQL). Another inspection approach is the skip-lot, or ANSI/ASQC S1 standard.[6] In this type of approach, only some lots are inspected and some parts of each lot are therefore inspected. A product that meets the qualification requirements for the supplier and the product (sections 4.1 and 4.2, respectively, of the ANSI/ASQC S1 standard) would be eligible for skip-lot inspection. There are certain rules to determine which lots are selected for inspection. Figure C.2 of the ANSI/ASQC S1 standard shows a simplified basic structure of the skip-lot inspection procedures. Finally, in the dock-to-stock approach, no lots and no parts are inspected; that is, as parts are received, they go directly to the inventory without any inspection at all.

Table 2.2 Sampling approaches for incoming inspection for attributes.

Inspection approach	Sampling amount
100% inspection	All lots, all parts
ANSI/ASQ Z1.4	All lots, some parts
Skip-lot	Some lots, some parts
Dock-to-stock	No lots, no parts

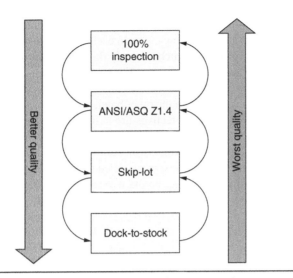

Figure 2.4   Switching between approaches for incoming inspection.

It is important to notice that these procedures are intended only for a continuing series of lots or batches and are not to be used for isolated lots. For these isolated lots, the ANSI/ASQC Q3 standard is preferred.[7] Continuous series of lots or batches is production at a steady rate. Production shall be considered continuous if at least one lot of product is submitted for inspection at a production frequency as agreed to by both the supplier and the responsible authority. If no production frequency is specified, at least one lot shall be submitted each month. Product shipped to other parties or products of a similar nature are considered in the determination of "continuous" unless excluded by both the supplier and responsible authority.

So, how could we switch between these inspection approaches? Figure 2.4 shows a diagram in which we can establish rules to switch between the different inspection approaches. For example, as quality gets better, we could switch between the following inspection schemes:

100% Inspection → ANSI/ASQ Z1.4 → Skip-Lot → Dock-to-Stock

On the other side, as quality becomes worse, we could switch between the following inspection schemes:

Dock-to-Stock → Skip-Lot → ANSI/ASQ Z1.4 → 100% Inspection

Before implementing any of these approaches, it is important to take a first look at any restriction imposed by either a regulation or a standard. For example, section 211.84 of the regulation for finished pharmaceuticals[8] (testing and approval or rejection of components, drug product containers, and closures) establishes that:

a) Each lot of components, drug product containers, and closures shall be withheld from use until the lot has been sampled, tested, or examined, as appropriate, and released for use by the quality control unit.

b) Representative samples of each shipment of each lot shall be collected for testing or examination. The number of containers to be sampled, and the amount of material to be taken from each container, shall be based upon appropriate criteria such as statistical criteria for component variability, confidence levels, and degree of precision desired, the past quality history of the supplier, and the quantity needed for analysis and reserve where required by 211.170.[9]

Based on this section of the regulation for pharmaceutical products, each lot must be tested before it can be released for use. So, skip-lot or dock-to-stock are not acceptable approaches for the incoming inspection of components, drug product containers, and closures. The same type of research must be done in other industries to determine if there are any restrictions in the use of any of these inspection approaches.

2.6 SUMMARY

Sampling is an important consideration in most organizations, especially when the sampling is destructive in nature. Organizations spend huge amounts of resources (personnel and economic) during inspection activities. Often, even with many samples, defective product is released to the customer. This is, in part, because the correct sampling approaches were not implemented. By implementing the correct incoming, in-process, and final inspection approaches, organizations can improve their inspection activities and provide a better product to their customers.

Although different sampling approaches were recommended for each stage (incoming, in-process, and final inspection), there are many other approaches at incoming inspection. The selected incoming inspection approach will assist in the reduction of the sample size, especially when the incoming quality gets better. The ANSI/ASQ Z1.4 standard uses different inspection schemes through the switching rules: normal, tightened, and reduced. The reduced inspection is a feature of Z1.4 permitting smaller sample sizes than used in normal inspection. It may be used while the product is in the lot-by-lot inspection state or skip-lot interrupt state but should not be used during the skip-lot inspection state. Skip-lot sampling may be used in place of reduced inspection if it is more cost-effective to do so. Finally, dock-to-stock could be implemented when the incoming quality reaches astounding levels. But, remember to do your research first, to determine if there are any restrictions imposed by a regulation or standard in the use of any of these inspection approaches.

NOTES

1. Manuel E. Peña-Rodríguez, "Serious about Samples," ASQ *Quality Progress* (April 2018): 18–23.
2. Genichi Taguchi, Subir Chowdhury, and Yuin Wu, *Taguchi's Quality Engineering Handbook* (Hoboken, NJ: John Wiley & Sons, 2005).
3. ANSI/ASQ Z1.4-2003 (R2013), *Sampling procedures and tables for inspection by attributes.*
4. ANSI/ASQ Z1.9-2003 (R2013), *Sampling procedures and tables for inspection by variables for percent nonconforming.*
5. Nicholas L. Squeglia, *Zero Acceptance Number Sampling Plans*, 5th ed. (Milwaukee: ASQ Quality Press, 2008).
6. ANSI/ASQC S1 (2012), *An attribute skip-lot sampling program.*
7. ANSI/ASQC Q3 (1988), *Sampling procedures and tables for inspection of isolated lots by attributes.*
8. 21 CFR § 211.84—Testing and approval or rejection of components, drug product containers, and closures.
9. 21 CFR § 211.170—Reserve samples.

3

Process Variation

3.1 OVERVIEW

Variation is an inherent part of every process. Usually, we measure the accepted variation, considering only how much the process varies when compared to the customer specifications. In the previous chapter, Figure 2.1 showed two interpretations of this variation. The diagram on the left of Figure 2.1 shows that, as long as the process is within the customer specification limits, we do not have any monetary losses. Once the process gets outside the customer specifications, then we begin to accrue monetary losses.

However, as per quality guru Genichi Taguchi, monetary losses start as soon as our process starts to shift away from the target value.[1] Furthermore, Taguchi mentioned that those monetary losses were experienced by society. As we move farther away from the target value, the monetary losses increase, following a quadratic function. Let us explain the concept with an example:

A company is dedicated to the bottling of soft drinks. Its engineering department sets a target value and tolerances for the amount of soft drink that each bottle must contain. If the engineers only focus on being within the specification limits (pass or fail decision), they will never learn about the monetary loss incurred whenever a bottle deviates from its target value (left-hand chart of Figure 2.1). In contrast, if they use the Taguchi model (right-hand chart of Figure 2.1), they can conclude that society will experience a monetary loss. How? Let us see.

If their process is continuously overfilling the bottles, they will be incurring an excessive use of material (soft drink). So, when the yield of material usage is calculated, they will see a negative accounting variance. That is, to produce a certain number of bottles they would have used a certain amount of soft drink. But, because of the overfilling, the direct material cost will be higher.

The profit formula is *Profit = Price − Cost*. So, if *cost* increases and they want to keep the same *profit*, then *price* has to be increased. And who do you think will be impacted by the price increase? Society, of course.

If their process is continuously filling the bottles below the right level, the accounting variance for materials will be positive. Now direct material cost will be lower and profit will be higher. However, what is the problem with filling the bottles below the right level? Besides being a misbranded product issue (which is a regulatory issue), there will be dissatisfied customers. In this case, dissatisfied customers will not purchase the product anymore. This will result in lower sales and, consequently, lower profits. If the company wants to keep the same profit, what will it have to do? Increase the price. And who do you think will be impacted by the price increase? Society . . . again!

In this way, we can see that society will always end up paying for the process inefficiencies. Consequently, it is of the utmost importance to reduce the process variation. To reach that goal, we must identify what causes the variation in our processes.

3.2 THE CAUSES OF VARIATION

It is a well-known principle in statistics that every process is subject to variation. It does not matter how many times we perform a task or manufacture a product, there will always be small differences. Those differences can be attributed to the *common* and *special* causes of variation.

Common causes of variation are always present in processes. This type of variation contributes a small amount to the total variation. For instance, there might be a small lot-to-lot variation. The same variation can be seen operator-to-operator and within operators. A characteristic of the *common* causes of variation is that they are predictable. As we will see later, when a process is in statistical control, we can predict within which values the measurements of our process will be. Consequently, we can say that a process in statistical control is stable, predictable, and subject to common causes of variation.

On the other hand, there are the *special*, or *assignable*, causes of variation. As opposed to the common causes of variation, the special causes of variation are not always present in the processes. Special causes appear and disappear sporadically. The special causes are not predictable; they can happen at any time and do not necessarily provide us a signal whenever they are going to appear. A process out of statistical control shows common *and* special causes of variation. This type of process is unstable and unpredictable. An example can help us understand the concept of common and special causes of variation:

> An operator works on a molding machine. Each day, he arrives to work and starts operating his machine at about the same time. He uses the same material, from just one supplier. He also performs the machine setting and some minor maintenance tasks. Each part that comes out of the machine is not exactly the same. There are slight part-to-part variations. However, those slight variations are considered to be due to common causes, or random process variation.
>
> One day, however, the operator is absent. A replacement operator works at the machine during that day. Although both operators follow the same standard operating procedure, the machine setup is more an art than a science. That is, the setup is operator-dependent. The new operator does not have the same experience as the original operator. Additionally, a material from a new supplier was approved and started to be used on that day. Suddenly, the parts begin to vary much more than usual. The new operator starts to make adjustments to the machine until, unfortunately, it breaks down. Notice that many special (or assignable) causes of variation were present. The higher variation experienced that day was produced by the combination of those special causes.

Here is another example, to show the concept of having only common causes of variation present in a process:

> A new analyst was hired in the lab. One of his tasks was to take a sample of bottles from the warehouse, weight those filled bottles and plot the results in an $\bar{X}$ and R chart. (This chart will be explained further in Chapter 11.) The analyst noticed some slight differences in the weight of the bottles. Although all the results were within the control limits in both charts, the analyst opened an investigation to identify the sources of variation and fix the problem. The quality engineer explained to the analyst that all the variation he was identifying was due to common causes of variation and that the process was in statistical control. Some of the sources of weight variation the process was experiencing were related to:
>
> • Bottle-to-bottle variation
> • Cap-to-cap variation
> • Label-to-label variation
> • Nozzle-to-nozzle variation
> • And so on . . .

The quality engineer explained to the analyst that, as long as the process is in statistical control, no major adjustments need to be done to the process. Tweaking a process that is in statistical control will increase the variation. If further variation reduction for an in-control process is required, then other tools such as design of experiments (explained in detail in Chapter 10) can be used.

3.3 SUMMARY

The study of process variation is fundamental in the implementation of an effective system. We must identify and distinguish between the common causes and special causes of variation because each one must be dealt with in a different way. One of the major mistakes is to treat common causes as special causes, and vice versa. This will lead us to overreacting at times, while not reacting at all in other situations. The use of statistics can help us understand the type of variation present and which kind of action would be recommended to deal with that specific type of variation. Knowledge about the causes of variation is of paramount importance because each type of variation must be dealt with using a different approach, as will be seen when we cover the topic of control charts in Chapter 11.

For now, let us visualize what a typical control chart with only common causes looks like (Figure 3.1) and how it would look if there are also

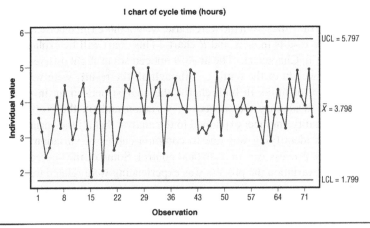

Figure 3.1   Control chart showing only common causes of variation.

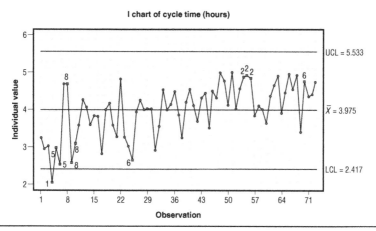

Figure 3.2   Control chart showing common and special causes of variation.

special causes of variation (Figure 3.2). Each of the labels in a data point in this chart represents a specific special cause of variation. Each of these special causes of variation will be explained in Chapter 11.

NOTE

1. Genichi Taguchi, Subir Chowdhury, and Yuin Wu, *Taguchi's Quality Engineering Handbook* (Hoboken, NJ: John Wiley & Sons, 2005).

4

Basic Principles of Statistics

4.1 OVERVIEW

To understand the causes of variation, several statistical concepts will be presented throughout the book. However, prior to going deeper into statistics, we need to learn some of the most frequently used statistical terms. *Statistics* is a collection of techniques used to make decisions about a *population* based on information taken from a *sample*. The population is the total set of data, while the sample is a subset of the population. As will be seen later, we generally take samples because measuring the population can be costly and/or time-consuming.

Descriptive statistics provide information about the data under evaluation. For instance, this information helps us understand the central tendency, the dispersion, and the shape of a set of data. By using descriptive statistics, we organize, summarize, and present the data in order to make decisions. Some examples of descriptive statistics are averages, medians, ranges, variances, and so on. *Inferential statistics* allows us to make predictions about the behavior of some data, using probabilities as a means to provide a degree of certainty to the decision we are making about the data. For example, whenever we perform a simple linear regression we obtain an equation that allows us to predict the value of a response variable (y) for certain values of the input variable (x).

We frequently find that terms such as *parameter* and *statistic* are used interchangeably. However, that is wrong. The *parameter* is the true value while the *statistic* is an estimate of the parameter. To obtain a parameter, we must measure the whole population. However, as mentioned earlier, measuring the population sometimes is impractical. For this reason, in most cases we just take a sample and estimate the parameter by calculating a statistic. Figure 4.1 shows the symbols used to define some of the most common

Metric	Parameter (population)	Statistic (sample)
Average	μ	$\bar{x}$
Standard deviation	σ	s
Variance	σ^2	s^2
Size	N	n

Figure 4.1 Symbols used for some parameters and statistics.

parameters and statistics. Notice that parameters are obtained from the population while statistics are obtained from the sample.

4.2 TYPES OF DATA

Prior to gathering any piece of data so that we may analyze it, we need to consider the type of data we have. In this way, we will be able to know which of the available tools can be used during the analysis of such data. To simplify our discussion, data will be split into three categories: discrete (attribute) data, continuous (variable) data, and locational data. *Discrete*, or *attribute*, data are things that can be *counted*. Also, they can be categorical or binary. Some examples of discrete data are number of defects, shift number, machine type, good/bad decision, and so on.

On the other hand, *continuous*, or *variable*, data are things that can be *measured*. These data can be subdivided into smaller portions. Some examples are weight, speed, temperature, and so on. This type of data provides more information than discrete data. For instance, it is not the same to say that a piece has one defect as it is to say how large the defect is.

Finally, we have *locational* data. This type of data shows where the characteristic we are looking for is located. For example, when we know where most of the defects occur, we might be able to arrive at a solution to the problem quicker. No data type is better than the others. Each data type has its own purpose. For that reason, the recommendation is to use a combination of the three data types to analyze problems and look for solutions to such problems.

4.3 SAMPLES COLLECTION AND SAMPLE SIZE CALCULATION

A *sample* is a subset of a greater set called a *population*. There are multiple reasons to analyze a sample instead of a population. Some of those reasons are cost, time, efficiency, and the use of destructive or nondestructive testing. The number of samples to take will depend on several factors, such as:

- Type of data (continuous or discrete)
- Purpose of data collection
- Knowledge about the population standard deviation
- Degree of confidence we want in our results (allowable risk)

The combination of these factors will determine the amount of data to be collected. For instance, continuous data (e.g., a measurement value) will require fewer samples than attribute data (e.g., pass/fail decision) for the same confidence level. Less data will be required for a cosmetic characteristic than for a critical characteristic. Also, the higher the variation of the data, the larger the sample size required. Finally, the more confidence we want in the results, the larger the sample size. Figure 4.2 shows an example of the kind of data collection matrix that is recommended prior to starting collection of data.

Each time a sample is taken, we need to consider a balance between the desired precision, the cost, and the sample size. For continuous data, we can use the following formula to calculate the sample size:

$$n = [(Z_{\alpha/2})(s)/(d)]^2$$

where,

$Z_{\alpha/2}$ is a constant obtained from a normal distribution table based on the allowed error

s is the estimated sample standard deviation

d is the desired precision

The following example will help us understand the concept:

Suppose we have a process in which we want to calculate the sample size necessary to estimate the average for the weight (in grams) of a specific part, with a precision of ±0.25 grams from its target. The historical estimate of the standard deviation is 1.0 gram. We wish to calculate the sample size required to obtain an average within that precision (±0.25 grams) with a 95% confidence level— that is, allowing a 5% error. Based on our analysis, the required sample size is 62 parts. Figure 4.3 shows a spreadsheet calculation for this example.

If we wish to increase the confidence level of our analysis to 99%, the spreadsheet tells us to increase the sample size to 107 parts, as shown in Figure 4.4.

Measurement/metric	X or Y	Type of data (discrete/continuous)	Data source and location	Sample size	Who will collect the data?	When will data be collected?	Graphical and/or statistical tools to be used

Figure 4.2 Data collection matrix.

Sample data:		
Estimate of standard deviation	S	1
Desired margin of error	delta/half-interval	0.25
Confidence level	100 × (1 − α)%	95.0%
Minimum sample size	n	62

Figure 4.3   Sample size calculation—continuous data, example 1.

Sample data:		
Estimate of standard deviation	S	1
Desired margin of error	delta/half-interval	0.25
Confidence level	100 × (1 − α)%	99.0%
Minimum sample size	n	107

Figure 4.4   Sample size calculation—continuous data, example 2.

Sample data:		
Estimate of standard deviation	S	1
Desired margin of error	delta/half-interval	0.10
Confidence level	100 × (1 − α)%	99.0%
Minimum sample size	n	664

Figure 4.5   Sample size calculation—continuous data, example 3.

If we would like to calculate the sample size for a precision of ±0.10 grams from its target value, we simply change the 0.25 value to 0.10. Applying the new precision to our example and keeping the 99% confidence level, our sample size increases to 664 parts, as shown in Figure 4.5.

So far, we have calculated the sample size for continuous data. However, if the issue at hand requires the use of attribute data, the formula to be used to calculate the sample size will be

$$n = [(Z_{\alpha/2})(p)(1 - p)/(d)]^2$$

where,

$Z_{\alpha/2}$ is a constant obtained from the normal distribution table based on the allowed error

p is the estimated proportion defective

d is the desired precision

Let us present the concept with an example:

> Suppose the historical proportion of calls answered within the established time frame in a customer service call center is 95%. The sample size required to see a margin of error of ±3%, considering a 99% confidence level (1% allowed error), would be 351 calls. On the other hand, the spreadsheet makes an adjustment based on the sample size and the proportion ($np \geq 5$). In this case, the spreadsheet recommends a sample size of 333 calls (see Figure 4.6).

It is important to realize that although the formulas provide an estimated sample size based on certain parameters, for the conclusions to be valid we need to consider the following factors:

- The data collected must be representative of the process (random).

- There must be no difference between the data collected and the data not collected.

- It is important to consider how, where, and when we sample.

- Sample from different times so that we can observe the different sources of variation of the process.

- Plot the data in a control chart to see if the process is in statistical control, which is a key requirement for many of the statistical analyses we will be performing.

4.4 DESCRIBING THE SAMPLE

Section 4.1 defined the concept of descriptive statistics, which provide information about the data under study. When using descriptive statistics, we organize, summarize, and present the data in such a way that decisions

Sample data:		
Estimate of proportion	P	0.95
Desired margin of error	delta/half-interval	0.03
Confidence level	$100 \times (1 - \alpha)\%$	99.0%
Minimum sample size	n	351
	np check (should be ≥ 5)	333

Figure 4.6   Sample size calculation—discrete data.

can be taken based on them. Descriptive statistics can be categorized into three groups:

- Measures of central tendency
- Measures of dispersion
- Measures of shape

The measures of central tendency show to which point most of the data converge. These measures can be subdivided into the following values:

- *Average (mean)*: the sum of all data points divided by the total number of data points
- *Mode*: the value that is repeated the maximum number of times
- *Median*: the value that lies in the central position once we order the data in ascending or descending order

On the other hand, measures of dispersion show how much the data points vary between them. Measures of dispersion can be subdivided into the following values:

- *Range*: the difference between the highest and lowest value
- *Variance*: the square of the sum of each individual value minus the average, divided by the population size (or by sample size minus 1)
- *Standard deviation*: the square root of the variance

Finally, the measures of shape provide information about the type of distribution represented by the data. One of the most common graphical tools used to visualize the shape of the data is the *histogram*. This tool will be presented in more detail in Chapter 5. An example of a histogram, along with descriptive statistics, for analyzing the data about the weight of a tablet (in grams) is shown in Figure 4.7.

The table to the right of the histogram in Figure 4.7 shows two measures of central tendency: average (mean) and median. It also shows two measures of dispersion: range and standard deviation (Stdev). Furthermore, the table provides information about the confidence intervals and the normality test. These topics will be covered later in the book.

4.5 THE NORMAL DISTRIBUTION

In statistics, there are many probability distributions, both for continuous data and discrete data. Among the most common probability distributions

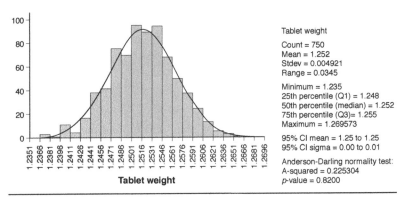

Figure 4.7 Histogram with descriptive statistics for the weight of a tablet.

for continuous data are the normal, exponential, Weibull, lognormal, and so on. The most common probability distributions for attribute data are the Poisson, binomial, and hypergeometric. This section will cover only the normal distribution.

The *normal distribution* has certain characteristics. For example, a normal distribution can be defined by the average (mean) and standard deviation of the population. Once we know those parameters, it can be found that 68.26% of the data will lie within ±1 standard deviation from the mean, 95.44% of the data will lie within ±2 standard deviations from the mean, and 99.73% of the data will lie within ±3 standard deviations from the mean. Later in the book I will use this concept to establish the statistical control limits. Yet another characteristic of the normal distribution is that the three measures of central tendency (mode, median, and mean) are the same value or, at least, very similar. Figure 4.8 shows the relationship between the mode, median, and mean for the normal distribution.

When data do not fit a normal distribution, those three values of central tendency are not the same. Figure 4.9 shows the relationship between the mode, median, and mean for a nonnormal distribution.

What is the importance, with respect to the central tendency measures, of knowing whether the distribution is normal or nonnormal? In a normal distribution, the mode, the median, and the mean are the same value. Consequently, any of these three values represents the central tendency. However, when data do not fit a normal distribution, the median is the best estimate of central tendency because the median is less impacted by those extreme values called outliers. An *outlier* is a data point that is very small or very large when compared with the rest of the data. Because the median only considers the position of the middle datum, the median is

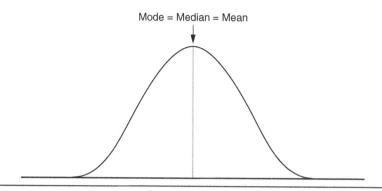

Figure 4.8   Mode, median, and mean in a normal distribution.

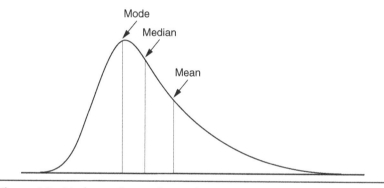

Figure 4.9   Mode, median, and mean in a nonnormal distribution.

not significantly affected by one or a few outliers. The mean, however, *is* significantly impacted by those outliers because each datum is considered in calculating the mean.

Consequently, one of the preliminary tests to be performed when analyzing data is the *normality test*. If the data fit a normal distribution, any of the three measures of central tendency can be used. However, if data do not fit a normal distribution, the median must be used as the measure of central tendency, not the mean. Those tests that use the mean as a measure of central tendency are called *parametric* tests, while those tests that use the median as a measure of central tendency are called *nonparametric* tests. These and other tests are discussed in Chapter 8.

Although in many cases it is convenient to have data from a normal distribution, this is not always the case. Figure 4.10 is a good example.

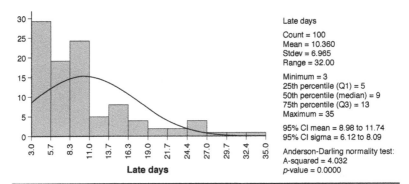

Figure 4.10 Histogram and descriptive statistics for nonnormal data.

Figure 4.10 shows the distribution of the data for late deliveries of a shipped product. Ideally, the number of late deliveries would be zero. However, if there are late deliveries, we want most of them to fall within a low tardiness value. What would happen if these data followed a normal distribution? Would that be acceptable?

4.6 SUMMARY

The concept of variation is of paramount importance in order to monitor and control our processes. The difference between population and sample, parameters and statistics, discrete and variable data, and so on must be well understood for an appropriate statistical analysis. A good sampling plan must consider factors such as type of data, process variation, confidence level, and precision required. We can establish confidence level and desired precision as we want. But process variation can only be reduced by using the adequate process monitoring and improvement tools. Whenever possible, collect variable data instead of attribute data because the former provides more relevant information than the latter.

To describe the sample, we need to know about the measures of central tendency, the measures of dispersion, and the measures of shape. When data fit the normal distribution, the mode, the median, and the mean (average) are approximately the same. However, when data are skewed, the average is significantly impacted by extreme values (outliers). In this case, the median provides a better approximation of the central tendency than the average. By the same token, when there are a few outliers, the standard deviation and variance provide a better approximation of dispersion than the range.

Finally, to analyze the data we can perform a graphical and an analytical evaluation. Chapter 5 presents some of the most common graphical tools used to start the evaluation of data. Just remember that graphical tools are the beginning of the analysis. The results obtained from the graphical tools have to be confirmed through the use of the analytical tools presented in subsequent chapters.

5

Graphical Tools

5.1 OVERVIEW

There are many ways to evaluate data. For instance, data can be analyzed practically. What does that mean? Evaluating data practically means that you just take a look at it and see if it makes sense. For example, is there any extreme value present? Can you see a "typo" error in the data? Any pattern? After the practical evaluation, the graphical evaluation follows. At this point in our evaluation, we rely on what the different types of graphs show. However, a graph alone does not present all the information required to make a conclusion. For instance, a histogram may show a "bell curve," but that does not necessarily mean that the data fit the normal distribution. To achieve these conclusions, an analytical evaluation of the data is required. This three-level evaluation of data can be defined as PGA: *p*ractical, *g*raphical, and *a*nalytical. This chapter presents some of the most common *graphical* tools used to evaluate data. Furthermore, many practical examples showing applications of some graphical tools are provided throughout the chapter.

5.2 HISTOGRAM

Let us start with the histogram. This graphical tool is very helpful to analyze *continuous* data. A histogram is a bar chart that represents the frequency of certain data. Such frequency is determined by the height of each consecutive bar. Using a histogram, it is very easy to graphically identify the central tendency of the data (represented by the highest bar in the graph) and the dispersion (the spread of the graph). Furthermore, using a histogram we can identify the shape of the data. Figure 5.1 shows a histogram for the diameter of a thread (in inches).

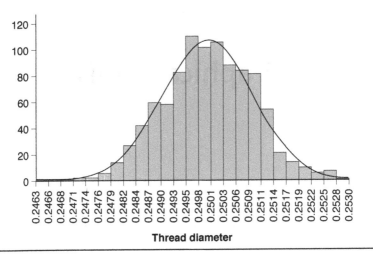

Figure 5.1 Histogram for thread diameter.

The histogram in Figure 5.1 shows the frequency for each of the dimensional intervals on a continuous scale. It also shows a normal distribution curve, which would represent that data if it were perfectly normal. There are many times in which we do not want to analyze the totality of the data but analyze them for certain categories. An example would be segregating the data by machine.

Let us suppose that data about thread diameter come from two different machines. Figure 5.2 shows the histogram for each machine in a combined chart. In this way, we can analyze the data for each machine separately. So, whenever we want to have a quick understanding of the central tendency, dispersion, and shape of data, the histogram is an excellent graphical tool to begin our evaluation.

5.3 BOX PLOT

The *box plot*, or *box-and-whisker diagram*, is another graphical tool used to visualize the data being analyzed. The bottom of the box represents the 25th percentile, the line inside the box represents the 50th percentile (or median), and the top of the box represents the 75th percentile. The lines spreading out of the box (the whiskers) represent the expected variation.

Those points beyond the whiskers represent outliers. Figure 5.3 shows the box plot for our thread diameter example.

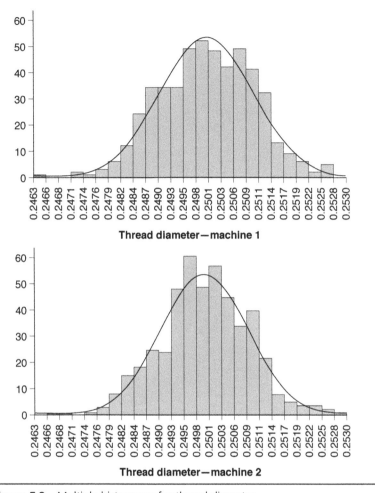

Figure 5.2   Multiple histograms for thread diameter.

As with histograms, box plots can be developed for the totality of the data or for different categories of data. Figure 5.4 shows multiple box plots for the thread diameter example.

While histograms are mainly used to visualize the central tendency, dispersion, and shape of the data, box plots are commonly used to compare the central tendency (median or average) and variation between certain groups. Box plots are also useful in identifying extreme values (outliers) in the data set. An outlier is an observation that lies an abnormal distance from other values in a random sample. This definition leaves it up to the analyst

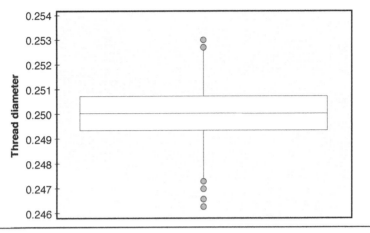

Figure 5.3 Box plot.

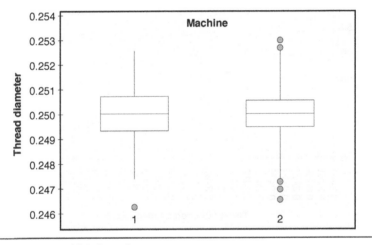

Figure 5.4 Multiple box plots.

to decide what will be considered abnormal. Outliers should be investigated carefully. Often they contain valuable information about the process under investigation or the process for gathering and recording data. Before considering the possible elimination of these points from the data, one should try to understand why they appeared and whether it is likely that similar values will continue to appear.

5.4 DOT PLOT

One disadvantage of box plots and histograms is that they do not show the individual data points. A graphical tool that shows each individual data point is the *dot plot*. Figure 5.5 shows the dot plot for the thread diameter data.

As with histograms and box plots, dot plots can be developed for the totality of the data or for different categories of data. Figure 5.6 shows multiple dot plots for the thread diameter example. Dot plots are also useful to identify outliers.

5.5 PARETO DIAGRAM

In section 5.2, the histogram was presented as a graphical tool for analyzing continuous data. The *Pareto diagram*, on the other hand, is used to analyze *discrete* or *attribute* data. Specifically, the main objective of a Pareto diagram is to *prioritize*. That is the reason the bars are represented in descending order. The most common Pareto diagram used in the quality arena is the *defects Pareto*. Used in this way, the focus of the Pareto diagram is to determine which defects have the greatest impact in our processes. Figure 5.7 shows a Pareto diagram for the packaging process in a manufacturing company.

The Pareto diagram shown in Figure 5.7 has two vertical axes. The axis on the left represents the frequency of each defect (represented by the height

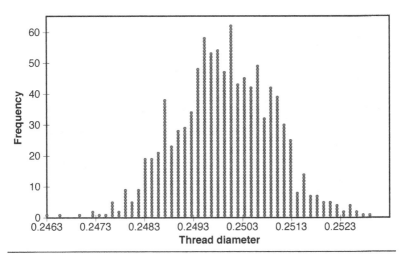

Figure 5.5 Dot plot.

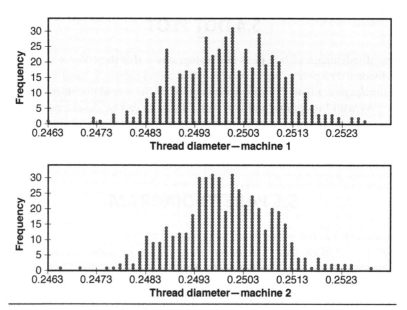

Figure 5.6 Multiple dot plot.

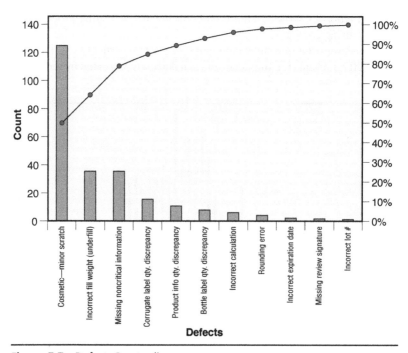

Figure 5.7 Defects Pareto diagram.

of each bar). The axis on the right of the diagram shows the cumulative frequency when we consider each additional defect. The cumulative frequency scale is represented by the line in the upper part of the diagram. The Pareto diagram in Figure 5.7 shows that "Cosmetic—minor scratch" is the most frequent defect while "Incorrect lot #" is the least frequent defect. Does that mean our objective would be to focus our efforts on eliminating or reducing the "Cosmetic—minor scratch" defects? Not necessarily. Why not?

Many times, the most frequent defect is not necessarily the one with the greatest impact or with the highest cost. For this reason, it is recommended to multiply the frequency by some weighting factor. Some examples of that factor could be cost, severity, detectability, and so on. If the company uses the *failure modes and effects analysis* (FMEA) tool, the weighting factor could be the *risk priority number* (RPN) obtained for each failure mode. More information about the practical use of the FMEA tool can be obtained from the article on "Fail-Safe FMEA," published in the January 2012 edition of ASQ's *Quality Progress* magazine.[1] For our example, Table 5.1 shows an example of the application of a weighting factor.

Table 5.1   Application of a weighting factor to the Pareto diagram.

Defect	Count	Weighting factor	Weighted count
Incorrect lot #	1	1000	1000
Incorrect expiration date	2	1000	2000
Cosmetic—minor scratch	125	1	125
Bottle label quantity discrepancy	9	50	450
Product info quantity discrepancy	11	50	550
Corrugate label quantity discrepancy	16	25	400
Missing noncritical information	36	10	360
Missing review signature	2	50	100
Incorrect calculation	7	25	175
Rounding error	5	50	250
Incorrect fill weight (underfill)	36	25	900

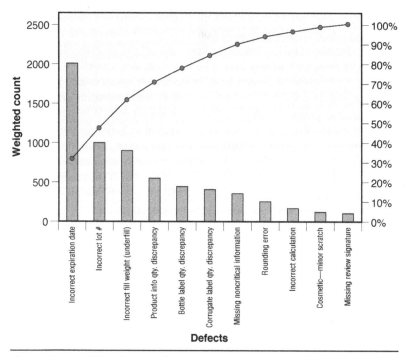

Figure 5.8   Weighted Pareto diagram.

Once the weighting factors are applied to each defect (multiplying the occurrence by the weighting factor), a new Pareto diagram is developed. Figure 5.8 shows the weighted Pareto diagram.

Looking at the weighted Pareto diagram, the top two defects now ("Incorrect expiration date" and "Incorrect lot #") are the two defects that appeared within the last three positions in the original Pareto diagram. Although these defects ("Incorrect expiration date" and "Incorrect lot #") occurred with the lowest frequency in the original Pareto diagram, based on their combined criticality-frequency weighting factor they are the most critical defects. Thus, they must be dealt with the highest priority. When we look at the line representing the cumulative frequency, it can be noted that eliminating the top three defects will eliminate about 60% of our problems.

In the previous example, only 11 types of defects were represented in the Pareto diagram. However, as the number of defect categories increases, the Pareto diagram becomes cluttered. One important feature of the Pareto diagram is the "Other" category. In this category, those defects with the lowest impact are combined in just a single bar. In this way, we can focus our attention to those defect categories with the highest impact. Figure 5.9 shows our Pareto diagram with the "Other" bar. This bar is always presented in the last position of the diagram, regardless of its height. Remember that "Other" represents a combination of multiple types of defects, but their impact is very low as compared to the other defects shown.

5.6 SCATTER PLOT

Many times, we want to know if there is any kind of relationship between two variables: an input variable and an output variable. In particular, we want to know if the relationship is *positive* (as the input variable increases, the output variable also increases) or *negative* (as the input variable increases, the output variable decreases). Also, we want to know if the relationship between those variables, regardless of whether it is positive or negative, is *strong* (dots are clustered around the regression line) or *weak* (dots are scattered on both sides of the regression line).

To determine if there is any relationship between two continuous variables, the *scatter plot* can be of assistance. In a scatter plot, we plot the input variable along the horizontal axis (the x-axis) and the output variable along the vertical axis (the y-axis). It is very important to note that in order to use the scatter plot, the data must be continuous for both variables. If the input variable (x) is discrete and the output variable (y) is continuous, the scatter plot would not be the most appropriate graphical tool. In this case, the box plot discussed in section 5.3 would be more appropriate. Figure 5.10 shows a scatter plot in which the tablet weight (input variable) is compared to the dissolution time (output variable).

Note that the relationship between the tablet weight and the dissolution time is positive. As tablet weight increases, the dissolution time increases. There is a strong relationship between both variables because the dots are clustered around the regression line. However, how strong is that correlation? Chapter 9 discusses the concepts of *correlation coefficient* and *determination coefficient* in order to conclude how strong or weak the relationship is between the variables being analyzed.

5.7 RUN CHART

So far, the graphical tools we have seen are mostly related to gathering information and showing patterns about the central tendency, the dispersion, and the shape of the data distribution. However, none of these tools consider the order in which the data were collected (e.g., the time when the

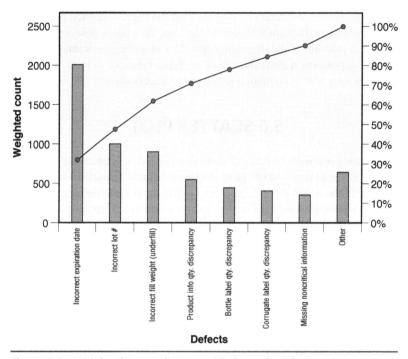

Figure 5.9   Weighted Pareto diagram with the "other" bar.

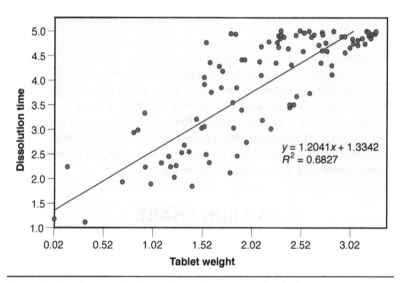

Figure 5.10   Scatter plot for tablet weight versus dissolution time.

data were gathered). Take a look at the histogram presented in Figure 5.11. It represents the diameter (in centimeters) of a pin used in an electrical component. As you can see, the data fit a normal distribution very well. When comparing the process spread with the customer specifications, the process performance index (P_p) is 1.40 and the actual process performance index (P_{pk}) is 1.34. More information about the process capability and process performance indices is presented in Chapter 7.

If we only consider the shape of the data, along with the process spread compared to the customer specifications, we might conclude that the process is capable, almost centered within the specification limits, and no further action is required. However, when we plot the data as a run chart (i.e., in the sequential order in which the data were collected), as shown in Figure 5.12, we are able to see an upward trend. Because the upper specification limit was established at 1.30, it will not take too long to have an out-of-specification value, probably within the next few weeks, if no action is taken to fix this issue.

Organizing the data using a time-based chart is of paramount importance when data are collected in a sequential manner. Whenever we analyze any kind of data, a combination of graphical tools is preferred over just one type of graphical tool. The appropriate use of time-based charts, like the run chart and the control chart, will assist us in determining when any kind of action is needed. They can also show us when a significant change has occurred in our processes. Let us analyze the run chart in Figure 5.13.

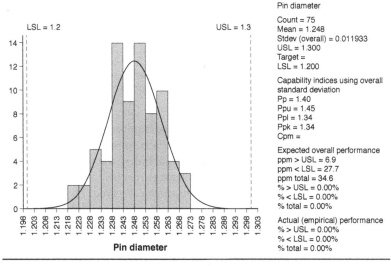

Figure 5.11 Histogram and process performance indices for pin diameter.

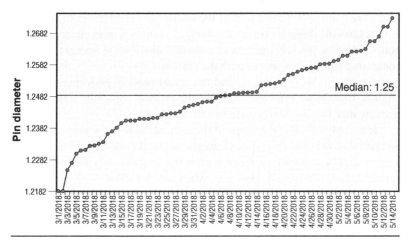

Figure 5.12   Run chart for pin diameter.

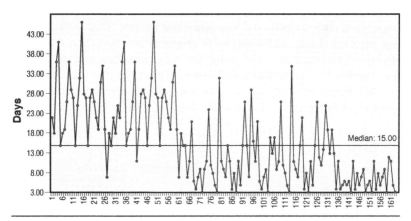

Figure 5.13   Run chart for days to complete a laboratory investigation.

The run chart in Figure 5.13 shows the number of days required to complete a laboratory investigation report. Each point along the horizontal axis represents an investigation (in sequential order); the value in the vertical axis represents the time it took to complete that investigation. Looking at the chart, at least three distinct patterns can be observed. The first pattern is observed for about the first 60 data points. This period represents the baseline, the period before the company started a massive corrective active and preventive action (CAPA) system certification process. The second pattern represents the period during which the company started to apply some of the tools learned during the CAPA system certification process. A sudden decrease in the time to complete the investigations can be observed in this period. Also, a slight reduction in the variation can be observed for the second pattern. The third pattern represents the period during which the company started to apply all the techniques learned during the CAPA system certification process. A slight reduction in the days to complete the investigation can be observed. Furthermore, a drastic decrease in the time variation can be observed during this period. This run chart can be used to demonstrate the decrease in the variation and median time to complete the laboratory investigations. Furthermore, it can be used to analyze the effectiveness of the CAPA system certification training.

Most of the available statistical software packages include run charts for analyzing different patterns. Among the patterns that most of these statistical software packages evaluate are clustering, mixtures, trends, and oscillations. Let us start our discussion with *clustering*. Whenever a cluster is observed in data plotted in a time-based manner, that clustering might be caused by specific situations. Clusters appear as too many consecutive points on the same side of the central tendency line (the median). Possible reasons might be changes in active ingredients, different shifts, different operators, and so on. Figure 5.14 shows a run chart in which different clusters can be observed. An investigation of the cause of those clusters revealed that a change in active pharmaceutical ingredient (API) occurred at several points.

The run chart is a graphical tool used to see these patterns. However, whenever we perform a run chart analysis using any statistical software package, a statistic called the *p*-value can assist us in determining if any of

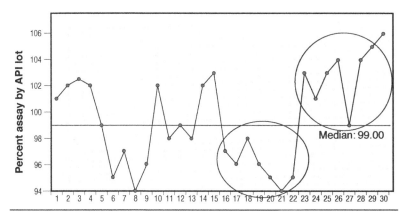

Figure 5.14   Run chart showing clusters.

the previously mentioned patterns (cluster, mixture, trend, or oscillation) is being observed. For now, our analysis will be based on a 95% confidence level (5% type I error probability, or 0.05). More details about confidence levels and type I and type II errors are discussed in Chapter 8. For our current discussion, if we find a p-value lower than 0.05 for any of these possible patterns, we will conclude that the pattern is present in our data. Similarly, if the obtained p-value for lack of randomness is lower than 0.05, we will conclude that the data are nonrandom. Figure 5.15 shows the statistical analysis for the API example.

As can be seen in Figure 5.15, the data show a p-value for clustering lower than 0.05 (p-value = 0.0048), which means there is at least one cluster present. Looking at the run chart (Figure 5.14), two clusters can be observed: points #16 to #22, and points #23 to #30. Point #27 falls exactly in the median and is not considered in the analysis. If point #27 fell below the median, a new cluster would have been created. As mentioned, the root cause for those shifts was the use of a different active ingredient. Looking at Figure 5.15, we can also see that the p-value for lack of randomness is also lower than 0.05 (p-value = 0.0096). That means the data are not random.

Figure 5.16 shows a run chart for data showing *mixtures*. An investigation into the cause of the mixtures revealed that hardness data came from two different machines: press A and press B. As can be seen in Figure 5.17, the data show a p-value for mixtures lower than 0.05 (p-value = 0.0046), which means there are mixtures present. Looking at the run chart for mixtures, two different populations can be observed: points above the median and points below the median. However, there are not many points close to the median.

Nonparametric run test: percent assay by API lot	
Number of runs about median:	9
Expected number of runs about median:	15.933
Number of points above median:	14
Number of points equal to or below median:	16
p-value for clustering:	**0.0048**
p-value for mixtures:	0.9952
p-value for lack of randomness (2-sided):	**0.0096**
Number of runs up or down:	17
Expected number of runs up or down:	19.667
p-value for trends:	0.1168
p-value for oscillation:	0.8832

Figure 5.15 Nonparametric run test showing clustering and nonrandomness of data.

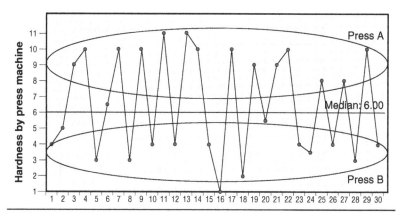

Figure 5.16   Run chart showing mixtures.

In a controlled process, we would expect most values to fall very close to the central tendency measure. However, in this case we can see a *bimodal* distribution. As mentioned, the root cause for this bimodal distribution is that hardness data came from two different press machines. In Chapter 8 we will use hypothesis tests to determine if these medians are statistically different or not. Looking at Figure 5.17, we can see that the p-value for lack of randomness is also lower than 0.05 (p-value = 0.0093). That means the data are not random.

Another pattern that can be analyzed with the use of run charts is a *trend*. This type of pattern can be observed whenever consecutive points show an upward or downward behavior. There are countless reasons for this type of pattern. A very common root cause for this type of trend is machine wear out. Figure 5.18 shows the behavior of a pin diameter (in millimeters) as the machine's blade was replaced due to wear out. You can see that, until the blade has been used on a certain number of pieces, the diameter does not stabilize. This happens at around value #15. From that point on, the pin diameter showed a random pattern.

As can be seen in Figure 5.19, the data show a p-value for trends lower than 0.05 (p-value = 0.0015), which means there are trends present. Looking at the run chart (Figure 5.18), an upward trend can be observed for the first 11 values. Then, for the next three values there were some ups and downs. Afterward, the process stabilized and started to behave in a random pattern. Based on this behavior, we can establish that the first 15 parts after a blade change have to be scrapped.

Finally, the other type of pattern evaluated by most statistical software packages is *oscillation*. This type of pattern is characterized by too many consecutive jumps from one side of the central tendency line to the other

Nonparametric run test: hardness by press machine	
Number of runs about median:	23
Expected number of runs about median:	16
Number of points above median:	15
Number of points equal to or below median:	15
p-value for clustering:	0.9954
p-value for mixtures:	**0.0046**
p-value for lack of randomness (2-sided):	**0.0093**
Number of runs up or down:	22
Expected number of runs up or down:	19.667
p-value for trends:	0.8514
p-value for oscillation:	0.1486

Figure 5.17 Nonparametric run test showing mixtures and nonrandomness of data.

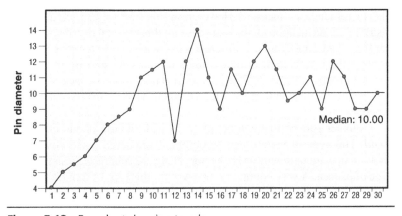

Figure 5.18 Run chart showing trends.

side. This could be the result of overadjustment, which is what happened with the data shown in Figure 5.20.

A manufacturer of colored paper strips was having quality problems related to strip length. An investigation revealed that the root cause of such high variation was machine overadjustment caused by a faulty sensor. Figure 5.21 shows a *p*-value for oscillation lower than 0.05 (*p*-value $= 0.0086$), which indicates that this pattern is being observed. After the faulty sensor was replaced, the length of the strip was controlled.

This chapter has introduced the run chart as a graphical tool to identify clusters, mixtures, trends, and oscillations. These analyses will be combined with the hypothesis tests to be presented in Chapter 8.

Nonparametric run test: pin diameter	
Number of runs about median:	13
Expected number of runs about median:	15.733
Number of points above median:	13
Number of points equal to or below median:	17
p-value for clustering:	0.1504
p-value for mixtures:	0.8496
p-value for lack of randomness (2-sided):	0.3008
Number of runs up or down:	13
Expected number of runs up or down:	19.667
p-value for trends:	**0.0015**
p-value for oscillation:	0.9985

Figure 5.19   Nonparametric run test showing trends and randomness of data

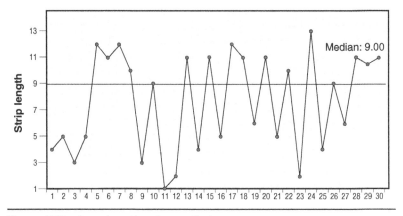

Figure 5.20   Run chart showing oscillations.

5.8 NORMALITY TEST

Section 5.2 of this chapter introduced the histogram as a graphical tool to show the shape of a data distribution. We learned how the histogram also shows the normal distribution curve to determine how well the data under study fit the normal distribution. Furthermore, using the histogram with descriptive statistics, we were able to see the estimates for central tendency, such as mean and median.

However, so far we have not examined, in detail, one of the tests performed when using the histogram with a descriptive statistics chart available

Nonparametric run test: strip length	
Number of runs about median:	16
Expected number of runs about median:	15.933
Number of points above median:	14
Number of points equal to or below median:	16
p-value for clustering:	0.5099
p-value for mixtures:	0.4901
p-value for lack of randomness (2-sided):	0.9801
Number of runs up or down:	25
Expected number of runs up or down:	19.667
p-value for trends:	0.9914
p-value for oscillation:	**0.0086**

Figure 5.21   Nonparametric run test showing oscillations and randomness of data.

in most statistical software. That test is called the *Anderson-Darling normality test*. As will be discussed in greater detail in Chapter 8, whenever a p-value is lower than a specified probability (0.05, for illustrative purposes in our examples), a statistical hypothesis called the *null hypothesis* will be rejected. In that case, another statistical hypothesis called the *alternate hypothesis* will be accepted. Whenever a p-value is greater than or equal to that probability, there will not be enough evidence to reject the null hypothesis. For the Anderson-Darling normality test, the null hypothesis will be that the data fit a normal distribution. The alternate hypothesis is that the distribution is nonnormal.

Figure 5.22 shows two histograms: One of them shows a normal distribution while the other shows a nonnormal distribution. The upper chart in Figure 5.22 shows that the normality hypothesis cannot be rejected because the p-value for the Anderson-Darling normality test is 0.0766 (greater than 0.05). At this point, it is important to establish that we are not saying the data fit a normal distribution perfectly. We are concluding the normality assumption cannot be rejected at this time. However, the lower chart in Figure 5.22 shows a nonnormal distribution. In this case, the data are so skewed that the normality hypothesis is rejected. This is evidenced by a p-value for the Anderson-Darling normality test that is lower than 0.05.

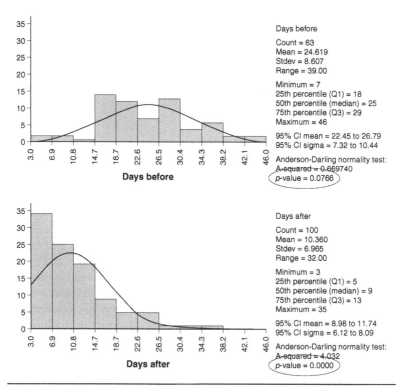

Figure 5.22 Normal and nonnormal data.

5.9 THE IMPORTANCE OF ASSESSING NORMALITY

So, why is it important to evaluate the normality of the data we are analyzing? In section 4.5, which introduced the normal distribution, I mentioned that when the data fit a normal distribution, the three measures of central tendency (mode, median, and mean) are very similar. However, when data do not fit a normal distribution (data are skewed), those three measures of central tendency could vary significantly. In particular, the mean (average) is the central tendency measure most sensitive to those outliers causing the skewness.

Whenever the central tendencies or dispersions of one or more distributions are going to be compared, it is important to evaluate the normality of the data. If the data fit a normal distribution, many *parametric* tests can be performed to compare means and variances. Some examples of these tests are one-sample *t*-test, two-sample *t*-test, one-way ANOVA, two-way ANOVA,

F-test, and Bartlett test. On the other hand, whenever the data do not fit a normal distribution, the tests mentioned do not have any statistical value. Instead, some *nonparametric* tests could be performed on the data. Some examples of nonparametric tests are one-sample sign, one-sample Wilcoxon, two-sample Mann-Whitney, Kruskal-Wallis, and Levene tests. The details for each of these tests, along with some examples, are presented in Chapter 8.

5.10 SUMMARY

Data can be evaluated in several ways. One common approach is to evaluate the data practically, graphically, and analytically. There are many graphical tools available. Each tool has its specific purpose. For instance, to look for central tendency, dispersion, and shape, we can use the histogram. Whenever we want to compare the central tendency of various groups, the box plot can assist us. One disadvantage of the histogram and the box plot is that they do not show the individual values; the dot plot can help us identify those individual values. If we want to prioritize the order in which we will address our quality issues, a Pareto diagram is a good option. Remember to use the weighted Pareto whenever the different categories do not have the same level of importance or criticality. To determine if there is a relationship between an independent variable (*x*) and a dependent variable (*y*), the scatter plot is an excellent tool.

Whenever data are collected in a sequential manner, they must also be presented in a way in which the time-based behavior of the data can be observed. The run chart is an easy-to-use chart to determine whether the data behave in a random manner or if some sort of pattern is being observed. Patterns such as clustering, mixtures, trends, and oscillations can be analyzed through the use of run charts. Finally, the normality of the data must be addressed because the use of certain analytical tools is subject to the assumption of that normality. If the data fit the normal distribution, certain tests (called *parametric* tests) are available, whereas if the data do not fit a normal distribution, other tests (called *nonparametric* tests) are available.

NOTE

1. José Rodríguez-Pérez and Manuel E. Peña-Rodríguez, "Fail-Safe FMEA," ASQ *Quality Progress* (January 2012): 30–36.

6

Measurement Systems Analysis

6.1 OVERVIEW

As mentioned in Chapter 3, every process is subject to variation. Such variation not only affects manufacturing processes, but any process. One of the least analyzed processes is the measurement process. The reason is not well known. People might not recognize the measurement process itself is subject to variation, or we might think that because of the experience of our analysts, they are not subject to improvements. Generally, whenever we want to reduce process variation, the focus is on the manufacturing process. However, the following formula provides some insight about the components of variation:

$$\sigma^2_{Total} = \sigma^2_{Process} + \sigma^2_{Measurement\ system}$$

This formula establishes that total variation is equal to the process variation plus the measurement system variation. In other words, the formula urges us to consider the variation produced by the measurement system separately from the variation inherent in the processes. To summarize the point, we do not want to mask the measurement system variation with the process variation because the two types of variation are independent and equally important.

The process used to identify the sources of variation in the measurement system is called *measurement systems analysis*; the tool used to measure those sources of variation is called *gage repeatability and reproducibility* (gage R&R). A gage R&R is a study in which several persons measure certain parts repeatedly in order to assess the *repeatability* and the *reproducibility* of the measurement system. Once the different sources of variation are analyzed, it can be determined if the variation comes from the differences between persons, differences in measurement methods, or the inherent difference between the parts. During a gage R&R study:

- Each person measures the same part several times.

- Data must be balanced; that is, persons must measure each part the same number of times.

- Units must represent the whole range of expected variation. It is recommended to select parts within the specification range—that is, parts from the lower specification limit, parts from the upper specification limit, and parts within the specification limits.

- Persons must measure the parts randomly. They must not know which part number they are measuring at any given time.

6.2 METRICS

Some of the metrics calculated in a gage R&R study are:

- *Repeatability:* The variation caused by the instrument. It is the variation observed when a person measures the same part repeatedly using the same measurement instrument.

- *Reproducibility:* The variation caused by the measurement system. It is the variation observed when several persons measure the same part using the same instrument.

6.3 PERFORMING A GAGE R&R

An example can help us understand the theory underlying the gage R&R:

A manufacturer wants to analyze its measurement system. The company produces plastic caps that are used in an industrial application. One of the most critical parameters is the inner diameter (in millimeters) of the plastic cap. To evaluate the measurement system, three analysts are selected. These analysts will measure 10 parts, and each part will be measured three times by each analyst. An excerpt of the matrix generated for the study, along with the collected data, is presented in Figure 6.1.

Figure 6.2 shows that 37.71% of the variation is due to the parts, while the other 62.29% is due to the measurement system (gage R&R). Furthermore, the 62.29% variation of the measurement system can be subdivided as 60.34% due to reproducibility (differences between analysts) and 1.95% due to repeatability (the instrument variation). So, if we want to reduce the

Gage name:	Cap diameter
Date of study:	06/15/18
Performed by:	M. Peña
Notes:	

Run order	Part	Analyst	Cap diameter
1	9	1	14.26
2	7	1	12.66
3	6	2	9.80
4	8	2	10.08
5	3	1	13.34
6	6	2	10.06
7	2	1	11.02
8	8	3	9.54
9	10	3	7.84
10	5	3	8.54
11	7	3	10.21
12	2	3	8.87
13	2	1	11.42
14	10	1	10.99
15	8	1	11.83
16	6	2	10.22
17	8	2	9.66
18	1	1	12.01
19	4	2	11.03
20	10	2	8.50

Figure 6.1   Gage R&R data collection matrix (partial).

measurement system variation, we could start by analyzing what is causing the differences between analysts.

Figure 6.3 shows that measurements taken by analyst #1 are consistently higher than those of analysts #2 and #3. An investigation of this issue revealed that analyst #1 was a recent hire whose training consisted of just "read and understand" the corresponding procedure. No other formal hands-on training was provided to this analyst. Furthermore, no effectiveness

Gage R&R metrics	% contribution of variance component
Gage R&R	62.29
Operator	60.34
Part × operator	0.00
Reproducibility	60.34
Repeatability	1.95
Part variation	37.71
Total variation	100.00

Figure 6.2 Percent contribution of each component.

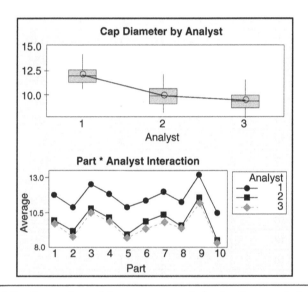

Figure 6.3 Comparison of the measurements for the three analysts.

evaluation of the "read and understand" training method was performed. Therefore, it was concluded that a root cause was inadequate training methodology.

A hands-on training module was developed and all analysts were retrained using the new methodology. A month after the retraining, the gage R&R was performed again with the same analysts. The results are presented in Figures 6.4, and 6.5. After retraining, Figure 6.4 shows that the variation due to the parts increased from 37.71% to 98.81%, while the variation

Gage R&R metrics	% contribution of variance component
Gage R&R	1.19
Operator	0.75
Part × operator	0.02
Reproducibility	0.77
Repeatability	0.42
Part variation	98.81
Total variation	100.00

Figure 6.4   Percent contribution of each component after retraining.

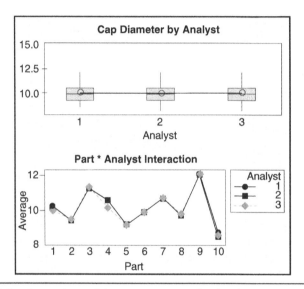

Figure 6.5   Comparison of the measurements for the three analysts after the retraining.

due to the measurement system decreased from 62.29% to 1.19%. It can be concluded that retraining was effective in reducing the variation produced by the analysts, in particular the new analyst. The same approach will be used for other test methods in which the training format is "read and understand."

Figure 6.5 shows how consistent all the analysts are after the retraining session. The box plot widths show that variation between analysts is very

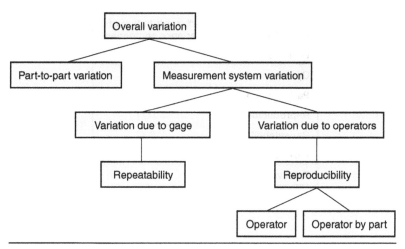

Figure 6.6   Sources of variation in a measurement systems analysis.

similar. Also, the centerlines show that medians between the analysts are very close to each other.

6.4 SUMMARY

Every system has many sources of variation. Variation can come from machines, materials, methods, measurement instruments, people, and the environment, among other sources. Very often, these sources of variation are divided into two broad categories: the variation caused by the process (part-to-part variation) and the variation caused by the measurement system. Specifically, the variation caused by the measurement system is divided into two subcategories: repeatability and reproducibility. Before engaging in any process variation reduction project, the sources of variability in the measurement system must be identified and reduced. Figure 6.6 summarizes the different sources of variation in our measurement system analysis.

7

Process Capability

7.1 OVERVIEW

Once the variation due to the measurement system has been minimized, we can measure the capability of our process to produce parts within the specification limits. The tool used to compare the process variation against the customer specifications is called the *process capability analysis*.

To understand the concept of process capability, we need to consider two important aspects: first, the variation inherent in our process, known as *process spread*, and second, the variation allowed by the customer, known as *process specifications*. A process capability analysis combines both—that is, how much the process varies and how much the customer allows it to vary—into a single graph. The process spread, also known as the *voice of the process*, is quantified by the standard deviation, σ. Particularly, the voice of the process is defined by the interval of $\pm3\sigma$ from the mean. As mentioned in section 4.5, in a normal distribution about 99.73% of the data is expected to fall within $\pm3\sigma$ from the mean. Specifically, in Chapter 11 we will use the "$\pm3\sigma$ *from the mean*" concept to calculate the limits for the control charts. On the other hand, the *voice of the customer* is defined by the process specifications, particularly, the lower specification limit (LSL) and the upper specification limit (USL). Figure 7.1 shows the process capability concept.

As long as the process spread is narrower than the process specifications, we can say the process is *capable*, as shown in Figure 7.2. However, when the process spread is wider than the process specifications, we say the process is *incapable*, as shown in Figure 7.3.

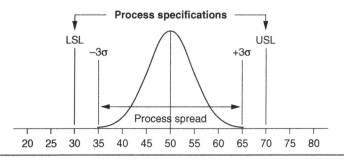

Figure 7.1   Voice of the process versus voice of the customer.

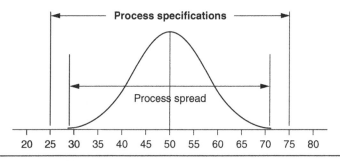

Figure 7.2   Capable process.

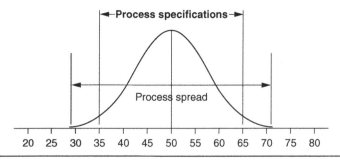

Figure 7.3   Incapable process.

7.2 PROCESS CAPABILITY AND PROCESS PERFORMANCE INDICES

To measure the process capability, we generally use four indices. These indices are known as C_p, C_{pk}, P_p, and P_{pk}. The former two indices, C_p and C_{pk}, are referred as *capability indices*, whereas the latter two indices, P_p and P_{pk}, are known as *performance indices*. The C_p and P_p indices are used whenever the process is centered, whereas the C_{pk} and P_{pk} indices are used whenever the process is not centered—that is, when the average is closer to one of the specification limits than the other. In this case, we will calculate two indices, C_{pk} upper and C_{pk} lower (or P_{pk} upper and P_{pk} lower, whichever applies). Then, the index with the lowest value will be selected. The rationale is that the index with the lower C_{pk} or P_{pk} shows to which side of the specification the process is shifting—that is, in which side of the specification the process is producing more defects. When the process is centered, then the probability of producing defects is the same for each side of the specification limit. Of course, that assumption only holds true as long as the process fits a normal distribution. If the data are not normal, we would need to either transform the data or use a nonnormal capability analysis. These approaches will be discussed later.

So far, we have mentioned which indices apply when the process is centered and which ones apply when the process is not centered. But, when do we use the *process capability* indices, C_p and C_{pk}, or when do we use the *process performance* indices, P_p and P_{pk}? The answer depends on whether we want to calculate the index for the long term or for the short term. The next question is, what is considered long term and what is considered short term? The answer does not have anything to do with how long we have been collecting the data.

What determines the short term and the long term is the way in which we calculate the process variability that goes in the denominator of the indices. Actually, there are two variability indices we will calculate: σ_R and σ_i. The σ_R value is used to calculate C_p and C_{pk}, whereas the σ_i value is used to calculate P_p and P_{pk}. The formulas for σ_R and σ_i are, respectively,

$$\sigma_R = \frac{\bar{R}}{d_2} \text{ and } \sigma_i = \sqrt{\frac{\sum (x_i - \bar{x})^2}{n-1}}$$

Figure 7.4 shows the formulas that must be used to calculate each process capability and/or process performance index based on:

1. Whether the process is centered as compared to the specifications
2. Whether we want to calculate the short-term capability or long-term performance indices

One important issue to note is that when the process is stable, both the C_p and P_p indices should be very similar, as well as the C_{pk} and P_{pk} indices. So, the decision of which index to use must be based on the estimate of variability chosen: σ_R or σ_i. One important point must be stressed here: To

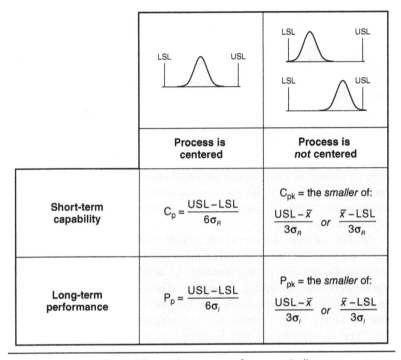

Figure 7.4 Process capability and process performance indices.

perform a process capability analysis, the process must be in statistical control. That assumption must be met for all the statistical analyses that will be presented throughout the book. As will be seen in Chapter 11, when the process is in statistical control, there will only be common causes of variation present in the process; that is, we will have removed all the special or assignable causes from the process. An easy way to remember this point is through the following adage: *There is no capability without stability.* So, before performing the process capability analysis and drawing conclusions from the calculated indices, make certain that the process is stable (in statistical control). This assumption can be verified through the use of a control chart. Most statistical software includes control charts as part of the process capability analysis. Remember, the next time you see a process capability analysis, ask for the control charts and make certain the process is in control. If the process is not in control, the calculated indices might not have any statistical meaning.

7.3 HOW TO INTERPRET THE PROCESS CAPABILITY AND PROCESS PERFORMANCE INDICES

Many times, we hear about the misuse of process capability indices. Some companies use only the C_{pk} index to determine when the process is capable while other companies use only the P_{pk} index to achieve the same goal. Neither C_{pk} nor P_{pk} can be used *alone* to determine how capable the process is. Each one (C_{pk} or P_{pk}) must be used *in combination* with the C_p or P_p in order to address the overall process capability. First, it must be understood that C_p and P_p only take into consideration the process specification versus the process spread, as shown in Figure 7.4. It does not consider the process centering. So, C_p and P_p will be used to determine process capability, regardless of process centering. On the other hand, C_{pk} and P_{pk} will be used to determine process centering, regardless of process capability. Figure 7.5 provides an example of different scenarios that we might encounter and how each scenario will be interpreted. This is very important to know because each scenario will require a different approach to improve the process. For this example, we will only compare C_p and C_{pk}. However, the same approach can be used for P_p and P_{pk}. Remember the difference between C_p (or C_{pk}) and P_p (or P_{pk}) is the way in which we calculate the process variability (σ_R or σ_i).

For example, in the scenario where $C_p = 0.75$ and $C_{pk} = 0.75$, we can conclude the process is not capable (because $C_p < 1.0$). However, because both C_p and C_{pk} are the same, we can conclude the process is centered. In this case, our problem is about process variation. If we want to increase both C_p and C_{pk}, either the process specifications must be widened (less realistic) or the process spread must be narrowed (more realistic). On the

$C_p = 0.75$	$C_{pk} = 0.75$	Not capable Centered
$C_p = 1.33$	$C_{pk} = 0.95$	Capable Not centered
$C_p = 0.95$	$C_{pk} = 0.75$	Not capable Not centered
$C_p = 1.33$	$C_{pk} = 1.33$	Capable and Centered

Figure 7.5   Interpretation of process capability and process performance indices.

other hand, in the scenario where $C_p = 1.33$ and $C_{pk} = 1.33$, we can conclude the process is capable and centered. This is the ideal scenario.

Furthermore, in the scenario where $C_p = 1.33$ and $C_{pk} = 0.95$, we can conclude the process is capable. However, because C_p and C_{pk} are not the same, we can conclude the process is not centered. In this case, our problem is about process centering, not about process variation. If we want to increase the C_{pk}, we must center the process. One misconception is concluding the process is incapable by having a C_{pk} index lower than 1.0. As mentioned above, if the C_p is high (e.g., $C_p = 1.33$) and the C_{pk} is low (e.g., $C_{pk} = 0.95$), the process is still capable because the process spread is narrower than the process specifications. In this case, the process is improved by just adjusting the centering. Here is an analogy to help remember this concept: As long as your car is narrower than your house's garage, you are capable of parking the car inside the garage, regardless of whether you center it. Not centering the car does not make the parking process incapable. The only fact that would make that process incapable is if your car is wider than the garage. In that case, even by centering the car in the garage, you will not be capable of parking the car inside the garage.

Finally, the worst scenario is presented where $C_p = 0.95$ and $C_{pk} = 0.75$. In this scenario the process is neither capable nor centered. If we want to improve our process, we must first center it. In this way, both C_p and C_{pk} can be increased to 0.95 without any further changes. However, in order to increase C_p and C_{pk} above the acceptable 1.33 value once the process is centered, we must either widen the process specifications (less realistic) or the process spread must be narrowed (more realistic).

7.4 PROCESS CAPABILITY ANALYSIS FOR NONNORMAL DATA

Very often, organizations deal with processes that produce nonnormal data. So far, our analyses have focused on dealing with normal data. But what can we do when we obtain nonnormal data from our processes? The two most common approaches are to transform the data (e.g., using a Box-Cox transformation or Johnson transformation) or to obtain a probability distribution for which the data fit. Out of those two approaches, we are going to develop an example using the Box-Cox transformation:

> Let us suppose that a pharmaceutical company is analyzing the assay percent parameter for a certain product. The first graphical tool the company used to analyze the data was a histogram and descriptive statistics summary, as shown in Figure 7.6. From the

Anderson-Darling normality test of such analysis, we can conclude the data do not fit a normal distribution. This conclusion is based on the obtained *p*-value for the test of 0.0478. As mentioned earlier, using a 95% confidence level, when the obtained *p*-value is lower than 0.05, we reject the hypothesis that the data fit a normal distribution. So, the normality assumption of the data is discarded. Figure 7.6 shows the data are positively skewed, or skewed to the right.

If we perform a process capability analysis erroneously assuming the data fit a normal distribution, we would obtain the results shown in Figure 7.7. The P_p index for such data would be 1.31, and the P_{pk} index for the data would be 1.30. Both values do not differ much from the accepted value of 1.33. Furthermore, we can say the process is centered between the specification limits because the P_p and the P_{pk} values are approximately the same. In terms of defective parts produced, the analysis shows approximately 90 parts per million defectives.

In fact, based on the results, we would conclude the process is doing fairly well, and with a small reduction in the variation we could obtain P_p and P_{pk} values above 1.33. However, the conclusion will be wrong because we assumed a normal distribution for the data when, in fact, the data are skewed to the right. So, to obtain a more accurate result for the P_p, P_{pk}, and defective parts per million, we will perform an analysis using a Box-Cox transformation.

Transforming data means performing the same mathematical operation on each piece of original data. The statisticians George Box and David Cox developed a procedure to identify an appropriate exponent (lambda, or λ-value) to use to transform data into a "normal shape." The λ-value indicates the power to which all data should be raised. To do this, the Box-Cox

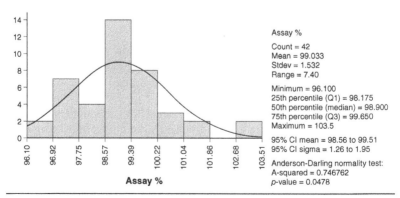

Figure 7.6   Histogram and descriptive statistics for nonnormal data example.

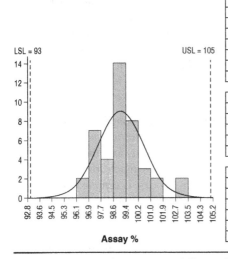

LSL = 93   USL = 105

Process capability report: Assay %	
Count	42
Mean	99.033
Stdev (overall, long term)	1.532
Stdev (within, short term)	1.399
USL	105
Target	
LSL	93

Performance indices using overall Stdev	
Pp	1.31
Ppu	1.30
Ppl	1.31
Ppk	1.30
Cpm	

Expected overall performance	
ppm > USL	49.3
ppm < LSL	41.1
ppm total	90.401
% > USL	0.00%
% < LSL	0.00%
% total	0.01%

Assay %

Figure 7.7   Normal process capability analysis for nonnormal data example.

power transformation searches from $\lambda=-5$ to $\lambda=+5$ until the best value is found. Using the Box-Cox power transformation in a statistical analysis software program provides an output that indicates the best λ-values.

For our example, a Box-Cox transformation was performed using statistical software, obtaining an optimal λ-value $=-5$. This means that all data values (Y) will be raised to a power of -5 or a transformed value equal to $Z=Y^{-5}$. The same transformation we performed on the individual values has to be performed on the specification limits, USL and LSL. A standard deviation will be calculated from the transformed data, and the C_p, C_{pk}, P_p, or P_{pk} indices can be calculated as shown earlier in Figure 7.4. Doing such calculations for the P_p and P_{pk} indices, we obtain $P_p=1.38$ and $P_{pk}=1.14$, as shown in Figure 7.8.

An important point to emphasize now is that, when we are dealing with normal data, all statistical software packages will calculate the four estimates for capability and performance: C_p, C_{pk}, P_p, and P_{pk}. However, when dealing with nonnormal data, only the P_p and P_{pk} performance indices will be calculated. This is because in the calculation of σ_R used for C_p and C_{pk}, a constant obtained from a table for normal data is required (the d_2 constant). However, in the calculation of P_p and P_{pk}, we use the formula of σ_i, which is the traditional formula to calculate the sample standard deviation. In the formula for σ_i, normality of the data is not a requirement.

The values obtained in Figure 7.8 ($P_p=1.38$ and $P_{pk}=1.14$) differ from the $P_p=1.31$ and $P_{pk}=1.30$ obtained in Figure 7.7, when we assumed the

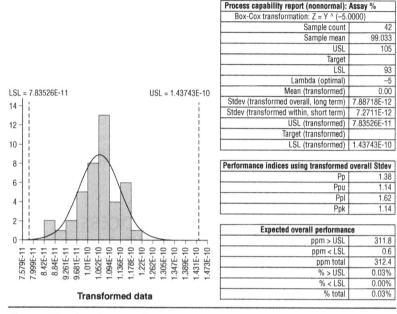

Table (right side):

Process capability report (nonnormal): Assay %	
Box-Cox transformation: $Z = Y \wedge (-5.0000)$	
Sample count	42
Sample mean	99.033
USL	105
Target	
LSL	93
Lambda (optimal)	–5
Mean (transformed)	0.00
Stdev (transformed overall, long term)	7.88718E-12
Stdev (transformed within, short term)	7.2711E-12
USL (transformed)	7.83526E-11
Target (transformed)	
LSL (transformed)	1.43743E-10

Performance indices using transformed overall Stdev	
Pp	1.38
Ppu	1.14
Ppl	1.62
Ppk	1.14

Expected overall performance	
ppm > USL	311.8
ppm < LSL	0.6
ppm total	312.4
% > USL	0.03%
% < LSL	0.00%
% total	0.03%

Histogram labels: LSL = 7.83526E-11   USL = 1.43743E-10; x-axis **Transformed data**

Figure 7.8   Box-Cox transformation process capability analysis for nonnormal data example.

data fitted a normal distribution. Furthermore, for the analysis assuming normal data, we obtained approximately 90 defective parts per million. However, based on the analysis with the Box-Cox transformation, approximately 312 defective parts per million are produced in this process. This is *more than three times the expected defective parts per million when compared with the first analysis.* Notice also in Figure 7.8 that everything has been subject to the Box-Cox transformation: the individual values, the mean, the standard deviation, and the specification limits.

Although the Box-Cox power transformation is frequently used to transform nonnormal data, it is not a guarantee for normality. This is because it does not actually check for normality. The method checks for the smallest standard deviation. The assumption is that among all transformations with λ-values between −5 and +5, transformed data has the highest likelihood (but not a guarantee) of being normally distributed when the standard deviation is the smallest. Therefore, it is absolutely necessary to always check the transformed data for normality using a probability plot. In our example, the Anderson-Darling normality test's *p*-value for the original data was 0.0478, and for the Box-Cox transformed data is 0.1549, as presented in Figure 7.9.

Anderson-Darling normality tests	
AD normality transformed data	0.541699
AD normality *p*-value transformed data	0.1549
AD normality original data	0.746762
AD normality *p*-value original data	**0.0478**

Figure 7.9   Normality test for original data and Box-Cox transformed data.

Based on this, we cannot reject the hypothesis that the transformed data fit a normal distribution.

7.5 PERFORMING A PROCESS CAPABILITY ANALYSIS

Let us now perform a complete process capability analysis to evaluate the current status of a process and evaluate the status of such process after an improvement project has been completed. Consider this example:

A yogurt manufacturer is facing some quality problems in its filling process. During the sealing process, some overfilled plastic cups are not sealing completely. To evaluate the current status for the *net weight* parameter, a histogram and descriptive statistics summary was developed. The summary is presented in Figure 7.10.

You will notice on the Anderson-Darling normality test that data fit a normal distribution; that is, we cannot reject the normality assumption because the value obtained in the normality test was 0.6216 (or greater than 0.05). An individuals and moving range (IMR) chart was developed in order to determine whether the process is stable and only common causes of variation are present. Remember that before performing a process capability analysis, you need to make certain that the process is in statistical control. Or, said in another way: "There is no capability without stability." The resulting individuals and moving range chart is presented in Figure 7.11.

Now that we know that only common causes of variation are present in our process, we can proceed with the capability analysis. Because the Anderson-Darling normality test in Figure 7.10 shows a *p*-value greater than 0.05, a normal capability analysis will be performed for the data. Figure 7.12 shows the capability analysis results for the net weight parameter.

As you can observe in Figure 7.12, the process is capable ($C_p = 1.47$); however, it is not centered between the specification limits ($C_{pk} = 1.13$).

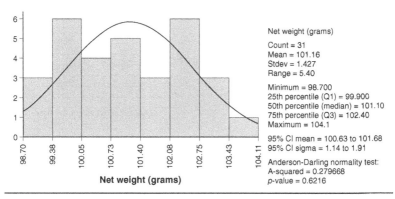

Net weight (grams)

Count = 31
Mean = 101.16
Stdev = 1.427
Range = 5.40

Minimum = 98.700
25th percentile (Q1) = 99.900
50th percentile (median) = 101.10
75th percentile (Q3) = 102.40
Maximum = 104.1

95% CI mean = 100.63 to 101.68
95% CI sigma = 1.14 to 1.91

Anderson-Darling normality test:
A-squared = 0.279668
p-value = 0.6216

Figure 7.10 Histogram and descriptive statistics for net weight.

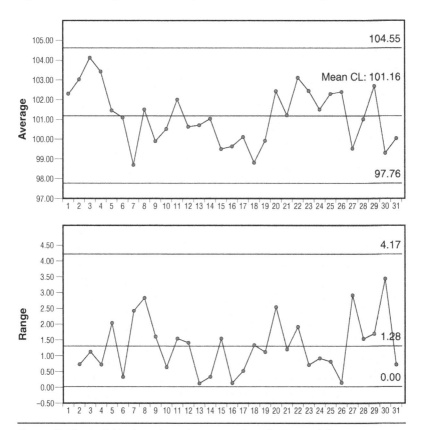

Figure 7.11 Individuals and moving range chart for net weight.

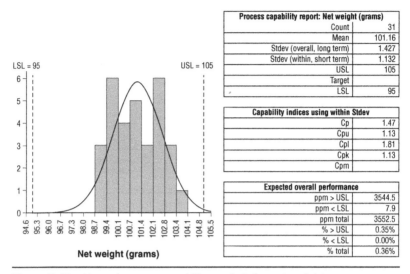

Process capability report: Net weight (grams)	
Count	31
Mean	101.16
Stdev (overall, long term)	1.427
Stdev (within, short term)	1.132
USL	105
Target	
LSL	95

Capability indices using within Stdev	
Cp	1.47
Cpu	1.13
Cpl	1.81
Cpk	1.13
Cpm	

Expected overall performance	
ppm > USL	3544.5
ppm < LSL	7.9
ppm total	3552.5
% > USL	0.35%
% < LSL	0.00%
% total	0.36%

Figure 7.12   Normal process capability analysis for net weight.

Furthermore, observe that the average is shifted to the right of the target value of 100 grams. It is such a shift toward the upper specification limit that is causing the overfilling situation and, consequently, the sealing problem. During a brainstorming session, the manufacturer identified that the process was intentionally set toward the upper specification limit because some complaints about underfilled plastic cups were received during the previous year.

So, the improvement team is faced with two opportunity areas: (1) eliminating the problem caused by improperly sealed plastic cups while (2) eliminating any possibility of a complaint due to underfilled plastic cups. After various design of experiments (to be discussed in Chapter 10) were performed, the proper machine settings were established in order to achieve the target of 100 grams while reducing the variation within the filling process. The results for the next 50 plastic cups filled after the improvement, along with the 31 plastic cups before the improvement, are shown in Figure 7.13.

As seen in Figure 7.13, a decrease in the net weight was achieved from the improvement project, as well as a major decrease in the variability of the filling process. To determine the effect of such improvements on the C_p and C_{pk} indices, a process capability analysis was performed, as shown in Figure 7.14. After the improvement project, the C_p index increased from 1.47 to 3.67, while the C_{pk} index increased from 1.13 to 3.67. Now the process is capable and meeting its target value. Furthermore, the defective parts per million were reduced from approximately 3,552 plastic cups not sealing adequately to practically zero, as shown in Figure 7.14.

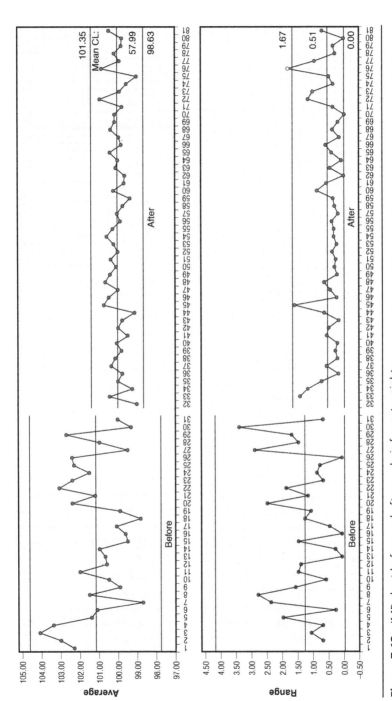

Figure 7.13 IMR chart before and after analysis for net weight.

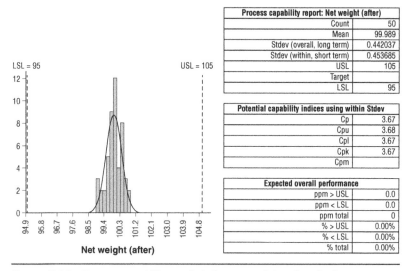

Process capability report: Net weight (after)

Count	50
Mean	99.989
Stdev (overall, long term)	0.442037
Stdev (within, short term)	0.453685
USL	105
Target	
LSL	95

Potential capability indices using within Stdev

Cp	3.67
Cpu	3.68
Cpl	3.67
Cpk	3.67
Cpm	

Expected overall performance

ppm > USL	0.0
ppm < LSL	0.0
ppm total	0
% > USL	0.00%
% < LSL	0.00%
% total	0.00%

Figure 7.14   Process capability analysis for net weight after the improvement project.

Now that we know how to evaluate and optimize our measurement systems and how to determine if our processes are capable, we can proceed to make comparisons between population means, medians, and variances through the use of hypothesis tests.

7.6 SUMMARY

The process capability analysis is used to compare the process spread against the process specifications and evaluate how capable the process is for producing within those specification limits. Before performing a process capability analysis, we need to make certain the process is in statistical control. To verify that such assumption is met, a control chart can be used. Remember that "there is no capability without stability."

Once we know the process is in statistical control, we need to evaluate normality of the data to determine if we are going to use a normal capability analysis or a nonnormal capability analysis (or maybe use a transformation of the data). The main disadvantage when using transformations is that all data must be transformed: individual values, mean, standard deviation, and specification limits. An alternative to the transformation is to identify, through a statistical software package, any other distribution that fits the data. Then, use that specific distribution for the analysis. Therefore, no transformation is required.

When performing the process capability analysis, we need to decide which indices to use: C_p and C_{pk}, or P_p and P_{pk}. Just remember the main difference in the calculation of these indices is which estimate of the variation was used: σ_R or σ_i. The σ_R is used to calculate C_p and C_{pk}, while the σ_i is used to calculate P_p and P_{pk}. But remember that C_p and C_{pk} are calculated only when the data fit the normal distribution. Once the indices are calculated, we can translate the results into defective parts per million produced by the process.

Those obtained results can then be used as a baseline for our process variation reduction projects. Let us start the reasoning for potential projects by making comparisons between different groups, using a tool called hypothesis testing.

8
Hypothesis Testing

8.1 OVERVIEW

A *hypothesis test* is a method of making decisions using data from our processes. In statistics, a result is called *statistically significant* if it is unlikely to have occurred by common causes of variation alone, according to a predetermined threshold probability called the *significance level*. Hypothesis tests answer the question "Assuming that the null hypothesis is true, what is the probability of observing a value for the test statistic that is at least as extreme as the value that was actually observed?" That probability is known as the *p*-value. In simple terms, the *p*-value might be interpreted as the confidence we have in the null hypothesis.

If the *p*-value is less than the required significance level, then we say the null hypothesis is rejected at the given level of significance. In other words, we do not trust in the null hypothesis. Rejection of the null hypothesis is a conclusion. This is like a "guilty" verdict in a criminal trial (the evidence is sufficient to reject innocence, thus proving guilt). Under this scenario, we might accept the alternate hypothesis. If the *p*-value is not less than the required significance level, then the test has no result. The evidence is insufficient to support a conclusion. In other words, we provide the benefit of the doubt to the null hypothesis. This is like a jury that fails to reach a verdict because guilt was not proved beyond a reasonable doubt. To summarize, here is a slogan you can use to remember when to reject or fail to reject the null hypothesis (H_0): *If* p-*value is low, the null hypothesis must go*. In other words, when the *p*-value for the null hypothesis is lower than a predetermined value, then the null hypothesis must be rejected.

Whether rejection of the null hypothesis truly justifies acceptance of the alternate hypothesis depends on the structure of the hypotheses. Rejecting the hypothesis that a large bite originated from a tiger does not immediately prove the existence of a gargoyle. Hypothesis testing emphasizes the

	Null hypothesis: Good lot	Alternate hypothesis: Defective lot
Decision: **Fail to reject the lot**	Good decision $1 - \alpha$ Producer's confidence	Type II error Probability $= \beta$ Consumer's risk
Decision: **Reject the lot**	Type I error Probability $= \alpha$ Producer's risk	Good decision $1 - \beta$ Consumer's confidence

Figure 8.1   Possible decisions in the acceptance or rejection of a lot.

rejection, which is based on a probability, rather than the *acceptance*, which requires extra steps of logic. When dealing with hypothesis testing, there are four decisions that can be made. Two of those decisions are correct decisions while two of them are wrong decisions. In statistics, those wrong decisions are called *type I error* and *type II error*. Figure 8.1 shows the concept of these four possible decisions, using an example about the acceptance or rejection decision to be made on a production lot:

> In any manufacturing process, the assumption must be that all lots produced comply with the quality requirements; that is, our null hypothesis is that the lots are good. Based on that assumption, the alternate hypothesis would be the opposite; that is, the lots are defective. Whenever an inspector is faced with a lot (good or defective), he or she can make one of two decisions: either to reject the lot or to accept the lot (which in hypothesis testing terms would be "fail to reject the lot").
>
> Taking a look at Figure 8.1, let us first explore the two good decisions. If an inspector receives a good lot and accepts it (fail to reject), it would be a good decision. The probability of failing to reject a good lot can be calculated as $1 - \alpha$, which we expect to be a very high probability. In this instance, the good decision will be called the *producer's confidence* because the decision will be

very beneficial to the producer of that lot. The opposite (rejecting a good lot) would be called the *producer's risk*, as I will discuss later. The second good decision in our example would be to reject a defective lot. The probability of rejecting a defective lot can be calculated as $1 - \beta$, which we also expect to be a very high probability. In this instance, the good decision will be called the *consumer's confidence* because such a decision will be very beneficial to the consumer of that lot. The opposite (failing to reject a defective lot) would be called the *consumer's risk*, as will be discussed later.

Let us take a look now at the two wrong decisions—namely, type I error and type II error. Whenever an inspector rejects a good lot, he or she is making a type I error. The probability of that error is established by a value called α, which we expect to be a very low probability. In this instance, the wrong decision will be called the *producer's risk* because the decision will be very detrimental to the producer of that lot. The second wrong decision in our example would be to fail to reject a defective lot. Such probability is established as β, which we also expect to be a very low probability. In this instance, the wrong decision will be called the *consumer's risk* because such a decision will be very detrimental to the consumer of that lot.

So, the obvious question is, "Which of these errors is more important to avoid?" The answer is that both errors are important. However, guarding against one type of error could result in an increase in the other type of error. The best strategy to reduce both errors is to increase the sample size in order to perform the appropriate hypothesis test. Doing so will allow us to detect smaller shifts due to nonrandom causes of variation.

Before performing any hypothesis test, there are some assumptions that must be satisfied. For example, when dealing with variable or continuous data, the assumption is that the data fit a normal distribution. If data are not normal, you would probably have to perform a transformation of the data, as mentioned in Chapter 7. When we are comparing groups from different *populations*, the following assumptions must be satisfied:

- Samples must be independently collected.

- Samples must be obtained randomly.

- Samples must be representative of the population.

When we are comparing groups from different *processes*, the following assumptions must be satisfied:

- Each process must be stable.

- There must be no special causes or shifts over time.

- Samples must be representative of the process.

Now that we know the basics about hypothesis testing, let us explore some tests to compare means, medians, and variances. Section 5.9 discussed the importance of assessing the normality of the data in order to determine which type of tests we have available to compare groups. When the data fit a normal distribution, the set of tests to compare groups is called *parametric* testing. When the data do not fit a normal distribution, the set of tests is called *nonparametric* testing. Let us start with the most common parametric tests, those used to compare means.

8.2 COMPARING MEANS

The four most common tests to compare means when the data fit a normal distribution are one-sample *t*-test, two-sample *t*-test, one-way ANOVA test, and two-way ANOVA test. The choice of test depends mainly with how many means we want to compare: one mean against a fixed value, one group's mean against another group's mean, or the means among three or more groups.

8.2.1 One-Sample *t*-Test

The simplest test is when we compare one group's mean against a fixed value. That fixed value could be a specification, a standard, a target value, an improvement value, and so on. Let us illustrate the application of the one-sample *t*-test with an example:

> Three months ago, a company hosted an extensive training session and implemented a new process to reduce the investigations closure time. The company wants to know if the training is paying off—that is, if the average closure time for the investigations has decreased significantly. Before the training session, average closure time was 20 days. Figure 8.2 shows the results of the one-sample *t*-test using statistical software.

Notice that the mean closure time of the first 100 samples taken after the training's completion was reduced from 20 days to 10.36 days. The question: "Is the observed difference the result of the training or just the result of common causes of variation?" The null hypothesis was established as a mean closure time equal to 20 days while the alternate hypothesis was

One-sample *t*-test	
Test information H_0: Mean (Mu) = 20 H_a: Mean (Mu) less than 20	
Results	**Cycle time (days)**
Count	100
Mean	10.360
Stdev	6.965
SE Mean	0.696531
t	−13.840
p-value (1-sided)	0.0000
UC (1-sided, 95%)	11.517

Figure 8.2   One-sample *t*-test example.

established as a mean closure time of less than 20 days, which is what we would expect. Recall from section 8.1 that the criterion to determine if the null hypothesis will be rejected or not is going to be the *p*-value. In that earlier section, I mentioned that "if *p*-value is low, H_0 must go." In our examples, for consistency purposes, I will use a producer's confidence of 95%, which means that $\alpha = 0.05$, or a significance level of 5%.

Taking a look at Figure 8.2, the obtained *p*-value = 0.0000 (not necessarily zero, but a very small number). We already mentioned that if the *p*-value is less than the required significance level, then we say the null hypothesis is rejected at the given level of confidence. In this example, we reject the null hypothesis and conclude that the observed investigation closure time of 10.36 days after the training session is significantly different from the original 20 days before the training session. Thus, it can be concluded that training has paid off because the investigation closure time has been reduced significantly based on the training session.

8.2.2 Two-Sample *t*-Test

If instead of comparing one group's mean against a target value we want to compare the means of two groups, then we cannot use a one-sample *t*-test but must use a two-sample *t*-test. As mentioned earlier, one assumption in performing a two-sample *t*-test is the data fit a normal distribution. Before performing a two-sample *t*-test, we also need to evaluate the variances of each of the two groups. This is an important prerequisite because the data-crunching process will be different for the case when the variances are assumed to be equal or when the variances are assumed to be unequal. To address the variances, we need to use an *F*-test or the Bartlett test, as will be discussed later in this chapter. The following example will illustrate the concept of a two-sample *t*-test:

> A company wants to compare the cycle time (in hours) for each shift to complete a specific task. There are two shifts: shift 1 and shift 2. During the following four weeks, the times to complete the task were collected and analyzed with a statistical software.

As mentioned, we need to evaluate each group's variance before performing the two-sample *t*-test. Figure 8.3 shows the results from a Bartlett test for equal variances. In this case, the null hypothesis is that all groups' variances are equal (or no significant difference exists between the variances), while the alternate hypothesis is that at least one group's variance is different. The same approach used for the comparison of the *p*-value with the significance level will again be used. Remember that we will be using a significance level $\alpha = 0.05$. Figure 8.3 shows that shift 1 has a standard deviation of 0.6967, while shift 2 has a standard deviation of 0.4719. Are they significantly different? Taking a look at the *p*-value, we can observe that it is 0.0218. Using a significance level of 0.05, we reject the null hypothesis and conclude the variances are different.

Once we determine through the Bartlett test that variances are not equal, we proceed to analyze the means of both groups. Remember that in the statistical software you use for the analysis, you will have to select a check box specifying "Assume unequal variances." Performing a two-sample *t*-test in a statistical software application, we obtain the results presented in Figure 8.4.

Bartlett test for equal variance: duration (hours) (Use with normal data)		
Test information H_0: Variance 1 = Variance 2 = . . . = Variance k H_a: At least one pair Variance $i \neq$ Variance j		
Shift	**1**	**2**
Count	31	42
Mean	3.526	4.306
Median	3.570	4.375
Stdev	0.696743	0.471918
AD normality test *p*-value	0.4241	0.2521
Bartlett test statistic	5.264	
p-value	**0.0218**	

Figure 8.3 Bartlett test.

Two-sample *t*-test: duration (hours)		
Test information H_0: Mean difference = 0 H_a: Mean difference ≠ 0 Assume unequal variance		
Shift	**1**	**2**
Count	31	42
Mean	3.526	4.306
Stdev	0.6967	0.4719
p-value (2-sided)	**0.0000**	

Figure 8.4   Two-sample *t*-test.

Notice the null hypothesis is that mean difference is equal to zero. In other words, the null hypothesis is that difference in the means is not significant. On the other hand, the alternate hypothesis is that mean difference is not equal to zero; that is, the means are significantly different.

Figure 8.4 shows the mean duration for the particular test for shift 1 is 3.526 hours while the mean duration for shift 2 is 4.306 hours. Is that difference significant enough? Taking a look at the *p*-value, the analysis shows that it is 0.0000 (not necessarily zero, but a very small value). Since the *p*-value is less than the required significance level, we say the null hypothesis is rejected at the given confidence level. In this example, we reject the null hypothesis and conclude the observed difference in test duration for shift 1 versus shift 2 is significant. Thus, it can be concluded that shift 1 is completing the test in a significantly shorter time than shift 2.

8.2.3 One-Way ANOVA Test

If instead of comparing one group's mean against a target value (or comparing the means of two groups) we want to compare the means of three or more groups, an *analysis of variance* (ANOVA) test can be used. ANOVA is a statistical test that uses variances to compare multiple averages simultaneously. Instead of comparing pairwise averages, it compares the variance *between groups* with the variance *within groups*. The *between-group* variance is obtained from the variance of the group averages while the *within-group* variance is obtained from the variance of the values within each group and then pooled across the groups.

As mentioned earlier, one assumption in performing an ANOVA test is that the data fit a normal distribution. Before performing an ANOVA test, we also need to evaluate the variances of each of the groups. This is an important prerequisite because for the ANOVA test, the variances are assumed to be equal. To address the variances, we need to use an *F*-test or Bartlett test, as will be discussed later in this chapter. The following example illustrates the concept of an ANOVA test:

A company wants to compare the performance of three shifts in terms of the manufacturing cycle time to determine if there are significant differences in their averages. After verifying the assumptions related to normality of the data and equal variances, the box plots shown in Figure 8.5 are developed. The dashed lines in the box plots represent the averages while the solid lines represent the medians. It can be seen that, *within* each shift, the median and average are approximately the same. In a normal distribution, the average, median, and mode are similar. So, the data appear to fit the normal distribution. Also, the variability *between* the three shifts does not differ significantly. So, we can see graphically how the equal variances assumption is met. Furthermore, the averages *among* shifts also appear to be similar; that is, no significant difference can be observed between the three shifts. Although the averages apparently are not significantly different, an ANOVA test will be performed to obtain a statistical solution.

The ANOVA table shown in Figure 8.6 presents the averages for each of the three shifts: 50.26 minutes for shift 1, 49.12 minutes for shift 2, and 47.44 minutes for shift 3. Is there any difference between those averages? The null hypothesis for an ANOVA test is that all the averages are the same (no sig-

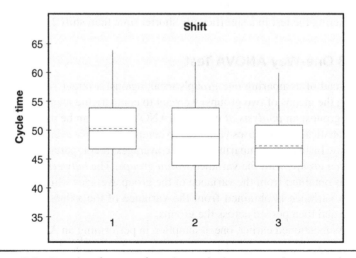

Figure 8.5   Box plots for manufacturing cycle time comparison example.

One-way ANOVA and means matrix: cycle time

Test information
H_0: Mean 1 = Mean 2 = . . . = Mean k
H_a: At least one pair Mean $i \neq$ Mean j

Shift	1	2	3		
Count	31	42	27		
Mean	50.26	49.12	47.44		
Stdev	5.721	5.865	6.296		

ANOVA table

Source	SS	DF	MS	F	p-value
Between	114.95	2	57.477	1.629	0.2015
Within	3423.0	97	35.289		
Total	3538.0	99			

Figure 8.6   ANOVA test for manufacturing cycle time comparison example.

nificant difference between the averages) while the alternate hypothesis is that at least one average is statistically different. As can be seen in Figure 8.6, the *p*-value for the ANOVA test is 0.2015. So, we conclude that there is not enough evidence to reject the null hypothesis. In other words, there is no statistical difference between the manufacturing cycle times for the three shifts.

Let me illustrate the concept with another example:

Although it was proved that the average manufacturing cycle time for each shift was not statistically different, the performance among the shifts does not appear to be the same. For that reason, the company developed a *quality index* to measure their performance. The index is based on a scale of 1 to 5, where 1 means poor performance and 5 means excellent performance. Figure 8.7 shows the box plots for the quality index of each shift. As with the manufacturing cycle times example, the averages and medians within each shift are very similar. So, the normality assumption can be observed graphically. However, as mentioned earlier, do not rely only on the graphical evaluation of the data; you need to perform an analytical evaluation of the data using the Anderson-Darling normality test or similar analysis. Also, variability between the shifts also appears to be very similar when analyzed graphically. But remember that in real life you will be analyzing the equality of variances through an *F*-test or Bartlett test, not just through a graphical analysis. However, when we analyze graphically the averages among the three shifts, certain differences can be observed, as shown in Figure 8.7.

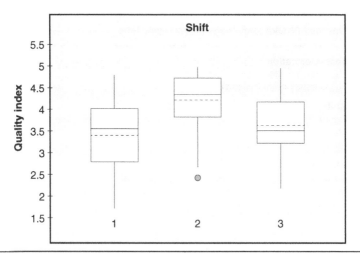

Figure 8.7   Box plots for quality index comparison example.

Taking a look at the box plots in Figure 8.7, a higher value for the average of shift 2 is noticeable. On the other hand, the averages for shift 1 and shift 3 do not differ so much. The statistical significance of this difference will be analyzed through an ANOVA test. Figure 8.8 presents the quality index averages for each of the three shifts: 3.39 for shift 1, 4.21 for shift 2, and 3.64 for shift 3. Is there any difference between these averages? The null hypothesis for an ANOVA test is that all the averages are the same (no significant difference between the averages) while the alternate hypothesis is that at least one average is statistically different. As can be seen in Figure 8.8, the *p*-value for the ANOVA test is 0.0000. So, we reject the null hypothesis. In other words, there is statistical difference between the quality indexes for the three shifts.

8.2.4 Two-Way ANOVA Test

What if instead of comparing different groups of one factor (e.g., machine), we want to compare different groups of two factors (e.g., machine *and* material)? In this case, we can use the two-way ANOVA. This analysis is an extension of the one-way ANOVA. There are two independent variables (hence the name two-way ANOVA). To perform this type of analysis, certain assumptions must be met: (1) The populations from which the samples were obtained must be normally or approximately normally distributed; (2) the samples must be independent; (3) the variances of the populations must be equal; and (4) the groups must have the same sample size. There are

---

One-way ANOVA and means matrix: quality index

Test information
H_0: Mean 1 = Mean 2 = . . . = Mean k
H_a: At least one pair Mean i ≠ Mean j

Shift	1	2	3
Count	31	42	27
Mean	3.39	4.21	3.64
Stdev	0.825	0.621	0.670

ANOVA table

Source	SS	DF	MS	F	p-value
Between	12.700	2	6.350	12.856	**0.0000**
Within	47.912	97	0.493943		
Total	60.612	99			

Figure 8.8 ANOVA test for quality index comparison example.

three sets of hypotheses with the two-way ANOVA. The null hypotheses for each of the sets are as follows:

- The population means of the first factor are equal. This is like the one-way ANOVA for the *row* factor.

- The population means of the second factor are equal. This is like the one-way ANOVA for the *column* factor.

- There is no interaction between the two factors. This is similar to performing a test for independence.

Let us explain the two-way ANOVA with an example:

A company is evaluating certain suppliers of a specific material to be used in its molding process. There are three suppliers for that material. Moreover, the company has four machines in which the parts can be molded, and each machine is from a different manufacturer. So, the company would like to learn if there are significant differences in the suppliers (materials) and the machines. In order to do this analysis, each material is used in each machine to produce a molded part. Then, a two-way ANOVA is performed. The first factor is *machine* while the second factor is *material*. Figure 8.9 shows the box plots for machines and materials.

The specification for the weight of the molded part ranges from 1.5 to 2.5 kg. The box plots for machine in Figure 8.9 show that the weights

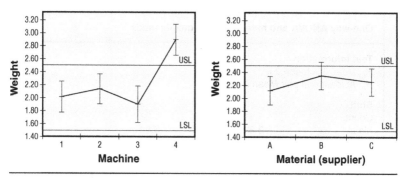

Figure 8.9   Box plots for machine and material example.

Two-way ANOVA: weight

Test information
H_0 (factor machine): Mean 1 = Mean 2 = . . . = Mean k
H_a (factor machine): At least one pair Mean $i \neq$ Mean j

H_0 (factor material [supplier]): Mean 1 = Mean 2 = . . . = Mean k
H_a (factor material [supplier]): At least one pair Mean $i \neq$ Mean j

H_0 (interaction): There is no interaction between factors X1 and X2
H_a (interaction): There is an interaction between factors X1 and X2

ANOVA table

Source	DF	SS	MS	F	p-value
Machine	3	11.951	3.984	12.960	0.0000
Material (supplier)	2	0.526059	0.263030	0.855689	0.4296
Interaction	6	1.295	0.215909	0.702395	0.6486
Error	67	20.595	0.307389		
Total	78	34.821	0.446418		

Figure 8.10   Two-way ANOVA test for machine and material example.

for machine 1, machine 2, and machine 3 behave in a similar way; that is, their average and variation are very similar. However, although the variation for machine 4 seems similar to that of the other machines, its average goes above the upper specification limit. When analyzing the box plots for material (supplier) in Figure 8.9, the weights' averages and variability look very similar. Figure 8.10 shows the two-way ANOVA for this example.

The null hypothesis for the first factor (machine) is that their averages are not significantly different, whereas the alternate hypothesis is that their averages are significantly different. Since the p-value for *machine* is lower than the significance level of 0.05 (p-value = 0.0000), we reject the null hypothesis and conclude that at least one of the machine's averages is different. Guess which one? Machine 4, of course. What about the material's averages? The null hypothesis for the second factor (material) is that their averages are not significantly different, whereas the alternate hypothesis is that their averages are significantly different. Since the p-value for *material* is higher than the significance level of 0.05 (p-value = 0.4296), we do not have evidence to reject the null hypothesis. Data do not show there is statistical difference between the averages for the materials. However, from a practical point of view, the box plots for material in Figure 8.9 show that material A is the one that produced a part that is more centered within the specification limits. So, from a business perspective, material A must be selected.

However, there is another aspect we need to consider: the interactions. As will be seen in Chapter 10, an interaction occurs when the behavior of one factor may be dependent on the level of another factor. In our example, an interaction would exist if the result depends on which combination of machine and material is used. The null hypothesis for the interaction is that it is not significant, whereas the alternate hypothesis is that it is significant. Since the p-value for the interaction is higher than the significance level of 0.05 (p-value = 0.6486), we do not have evidence to reject the null hypothesis. Data do not show that interaction of machines and materials is significant. In summary, the company should purchase material A and could produce the part in machine 1, machine 2, or machine 3.

8.3 COMPARING MEDIANS

So far, we have been performing hypothesis tests for data that fit the normal distribution. But what if the data do not fit a normal distribution? In that case, we can either transform the data or run a *nonparametric* test, as discussed in section 5.9. This chapter explains three nonparametric tests: the one-sample sign test, two-sample Mann-Whitney test, and Kruskal-Wallis test.

8.3.1 One-Sample Sign Test

The *one-sample sign* is a nonparametric test equivalent to the one-sample t-test. The nonparametric tests are performed whenever the data do not fit the normal distribution. Recall that whenever the data fit the normal distribution, we can use either the average, the median, or the mode as the measure of central tendency because all of them are very similar. However, when the data do not fit the normal distribution (i.e., the data are skewed), then we need to use the median instead of the average because the median is less impacted by outliers than the average. Let us illustrate the use of the one-sample sign test with an example:

The median closure time for investigations has been 25 days (50% of investigations needed more than 25 days to be completed). After new root cause analysis training, three months of data were used to evaluate the improvement in the investigation closure time (if any). Figure 8.11 shows the results of the one-sample sign test using statistical software.

Notice that the median for the investigation closure time of the 100 samples taken after the training's completion was reduced from 25 days to 9 days. The question might be: "Is the observed difference the result of the training or just the result of common-cause variation?" The null hypothesis was established as a median equal to 25 days while the alternate hypothesis was established as a median of less than 25 days, which is what we would expect. Recall from section 8.1 that the criterion to determine if the null hypothesis will be rejected or not is going to be the p-value: *If p-value is low, H_0 must go.* In our examples, for consistency purposes, I will use a producer's confidence of 95%, which means that $\alpha = 0.05$, or a significance level of 5%.

Taking a look at Figure 8.11, the obtained p-value $= 0.0000$ (not necessarily zero, but a very small number). We already mentioned that if the p-value is less than the required significance level, then we say the null hypothesis is rejected at the given confidence level. In this example, we reject the null hypothesis and conclude the observed investigation closure time of 9 days after the training is significantly different from than the original 25 days. Thus, it can be concluded that training has paid off because

One-sample sign test	
Test information H_0: Median = 25 H_a: Median less than 25	
Results	**Days after**
Count (N)	100
Median	9
Points below 25	93
Points equal to 25	1
Points above 25	6
p-value (1-sided)	**0.0000**

Figure 8.11   One-sample sign test example.

the investigation closure time has been reduced significantly based on the training.

8.3.2 Two-Sample Mann-Whitney Test

The *two-sample Mann-Whitney* is a nonparametric test equivalent to the two-sample *t*-test. The nonparametric tests are performed whenever the data do not fit the normal distribution. The two-sample Mann-Whitney test compares the medians of two groups. Let us illustrate the use of this test with an example:

> A pharmaceutical company wanted to determine if there are significant differences in the hardness of the tablet it manufactures using two different pieces of equipment. To do this analysis, data from one year of production was collected from each machine. After performing a normality test, the company noticed that the data did not fit the normal distribution. The histograms in Figure 8.12 show a *p*-value for the Anderson-Darling normality test of 0.0000 for each machine, indicating that the data do not fit the normal distribution.

Since the data do not fit a normal distribution, a two-sample Mann-Whitney test was performed with the data to compare the two medians. Figure 8.13 shows the results of the test in which a *p*-value of 0.0000 was obtained. A *p*-value lower than 0.05 for this test indicates that the medians of each of these populations are statistically different. The obtained value indicates the difference in the median (8.90 kiloponds [kp] for machine 1 and 9.10 kp for machine 2) is due to some special causes. Such difference in the medians is not the result of natural process variability. So, this issue must be investigated to determine why machine 2 is providing a higher hardness than machine 1.

8.3.3 Kruskal-Wallis Test

The *Kruskal-Wallis* is a nonparametric test equivalent to the one-way ANOVA test. The nonparametric tests are performed whenever the data do not fit the normal distribution. The Kruskal-Wallis test is used for comparing more than two samples that are independent or not related. The null hypothesis is that the populations from which the samples originate have the same median. When the Kruskal-Wallis test leads to significant results, then at least one of the sample medians is different from the other sample medians. The test does not identify where the differences occur or how many differences actually occur. It is an extension of the two-sample Mann-Whitney

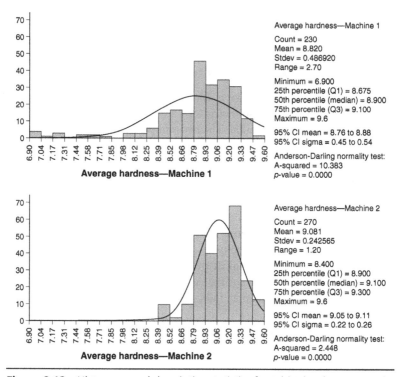

Figure 8.12 Histogram and descriptive statistics for tablet hardness example.

Two-sample Mann-Whitney test: average hardness

Test information
H_0: Median difference = 0
H_a: Median difference ≠ 0

Machine	1	2
Count	230	270
Median	8.90	9.10
Mann-Whitney statistic	46569.50	
p-value (2-sided, adjusted for ties)	**0.0000**	

Figure 8.13 Two-sample Mann-Whitney test for tablet hardness example.

test for comparing three or more groups. The two-sample Mann-Whitney test would help analyze the specific sample pairs for significant differences. Since it is a nonparametric method, the Kruskal-Wallis test does not assume a normal distribution, unlike the analogous one-way ANOVA. However, the test does assume an identically shaped and scaled distribution for each group, except for any difference in medians. Let us explain the Kruskal-Wallis test through an example:

A company wanted to analyze three different suppliers of a fluid used in its manufacturing process so that it can select one of them. A critical characteristic of the fluid is viscosity, measured in *centipoise* (cP). The specifications for the viscosity of the fluid range from 2.4 to 3.6 cP. Data from the three suppliers were analyzed, and a histogram and descriptive statistics of them generated. Figure 8.14 shows the results for the three suppliers. From the Anderson-Darling normality test, it can be seen that none of the three data sets fits a normal distribution because the p-values for them are below 0.05, the significance level (α) selected by the company. Because the data do not fit the normal distribution, we will use the median instead of the mean as the measure of central tendency, as mentioned in section 4.5. It can be seen in Figure 8.14 that the median for supplier A is 3.30 cP; for supplier B it is 2.98 cP and for supplier C it is 2.66 cP.

To analyze the medians, a Kruskal-Wallis test will be performed. The null hypothesis is that the medians are not significantly different, while the alternate hypothesis is that at least one median is different. Figure 8.15 shows the results of the Kruskal-Wallis test. A p-value of 0.0000 was obtained. A p-value lower than 0.05 for this test indicates that at least one of the medians of these populations is statistically different. The obtained value indicates that the difference in the medians (3.30 cP for supplier A, 2.98 cP for supplier B, and 2.66 cP for supplier C) is due to some special causes. Such differences in the medians are not the result of natural process variability.

Because supplier B has a median of 2.98 cP, which is closest to the target value of 3.00 cP, that supplier must be selected. Notice as well that data from supplier B have the smallest standard deviation among the three suppliers (Figure 8.14). However, the equality of variances when the data are not normal will be discussed in section 8.4.3 about the Levene test.

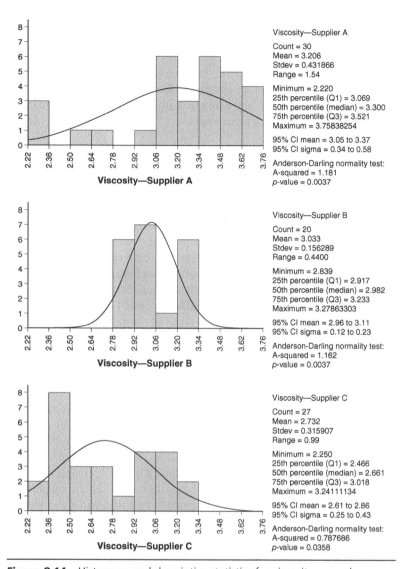

Figure 8.14 Histogram and descriptive statistics for viscosity example.

Kruskal-Wallis nonparametric ANOVA: viscosity			
Test information			
H_0: Median 1 = Median 2 = . . . = Median k			
H_a: At least one pair Median $i \neq$ Median j			
Supplier	**A**	**B**	**C**
Count (N)	30	20	27
Median	3.30	2.98	2.66
p-value (2-sided, adjusted for ties)	**0.0000**		

Figure 8.15 Kruskal-Wallis test for viscosity example.

8.4 COMPARING VARIANCES

Sections 8.2 and 8.3 were about the comparison of means and medians, respectively. Those are measures of central tendency, as discussed in section 4.4. However, as discussed in section 7.3 on process capability, sometimes our issues are not about process *centering* but about process *dispersion*. One of the measures of dispersion discussed in section 4.4 was the *variance*. This section now discusses three hypothesis tests for comparing variances: *F*-test, Bartlett test, and Levene test. The first two tests will be used when the data fit the normal distribution, whereas the last test will be used for nonnormal data.

8.4.1 *F*-Test

The *F*-test is used whenever we want to compare the variances between two groups. The underlying assumption is that the data fit a normal distribution. As mentioned in section 8.2.3, this test has to be performed before a one-way ANOVA because, in order to perform such a test, the variances must be equal. Let us illustrate the use of the *F*-test with an example:

> A company wants to analyze two different adhesives for the transdermal patches it manufactures. Adhesives on a patch generally help maintain contact between the transdermal system and skin surface. The adhesiveness of the patches is critical in the drug delivery mechanism, its safety, product quality, and efficacy. As such, a good adhesive should easily adhere to the skin with an applied finger pressure and be tacky enough to maintain a strong holding force. The adhesive should also be easily removed from the skin

without leaving a residue. The specification for the adhesiveness of the transdermal patch ranges from 300 to 3500 g/system. The box plots for the transdermal patches using each adhesive are presented in Figure 8.16.

Notice that although the averages seem to be similar, the variation in adhesiveness of adhesive A is smaller than that of adhesive B. To analyze the variances of these two groups, an *F*-test will be performed using a statistical software. The results of the *F*-test are summarized in Figure 8.17.

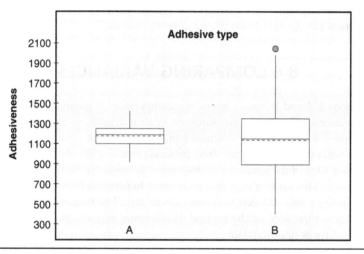

Figure 8.16   Box plots for transdermal patch adhesiveness example.

F-test for equal variance: adhesiveness (Use with normal data)		
Test information H_0: Variance 1 = Variance 2 H_a: Variance 1 ≠ Variance 2		
Adhesive type	**A**	**B**
Count	100	125
Mean	1179.2	1136.0
Stdev	102.62	335.57
AD normality test *p*-value	0.1975	0.7584
p-value	**0.0000**	

Figure 8.17   *F*-test for transdermal patch adhesiveness example.

As can be seen in Figure 8.17, the null hypothesis is that the variances are not significantly different, while the alternate hypothesis is that they are different. Since the p-value is lower than 0.05, we reject the null hypothesis and conclude there are significant differences in the variances. Adhesive A has a standard deviation of 102.6 g/system while adhesive B has a standard deviation of 335.6 g/system. Because the averages for both adhesives are about the same (1179.2 for adhesive A and 1136.0 for adhesive B), the adhesive with the lower variation must be selected. In this case, adhesive A must be the chosen one.

At this point, we might ask whether the F-test was the appropriate one to use for these data since we did not perform a normality test before performing this test. However, as can be seen in Figure 8.17, an Anderson-Darling normality test was performed as part of the analysis. The p-values for the normality test are higher than 0.05; thus, we cannot reject the null hypothesis that the data fit a normal distribution. If any of those p-values were lower than 0.05, we could not have chosen the F-test (or Bartlett test, for three or more variances). In such case, a Levene test would be the appropriate one.

8.4.2 Bartlett Test

The Bartlett test is used whenever we want to compare the variances between two or more groups. The underlying assumption is that the data fit a normal distribution. As mentioned in section 8.2.3, this test has to be performed before a one-way ANOVA because, in order to perform such a test, the variances must be equal. Let us illustrate the use of the Bartlett test with an example:

> Let us suppose that in the previous example the manufacturer would like to test a third adhesive. Since the F-test can only compare two variances at a time, we need to perform a Bartlett test. Figure 8.18 shows the box plots for the adhesiveness tests.

It can be seen that, although the averages seem to be similar, the variation of adhesive A is smaller than that of adhesive B and adhesive C. To analyze the variances of these three groups, a Bartlett test will be performed using statistical software. The results of the Bartlett test are summarized in Figure 8.19.

As Figure 8.19 shows, the null hypothesis is that the variances are not significantly different, while the alternate hypothesis is that at least one of the variances is different. Because the p-value is lower than 0.05, we reject the null hypothesis and conclude there are significant differences in the variances. Adhesive A has a standard deviation of 102.6 g/system, adhesive B

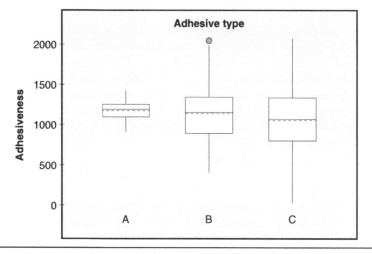

Figure 8.18   Box plots for transdermal patch adhesiveness example.

Bartlett test for equal variance: adhesiveness (Use with normal data)			
Test information H_0: Variance 1 = Variance 2 = ... = Variance k H_a: At least one pair Variance i ≠ Variance j			
Adhesive type	**A**	**B**	**C**
Count	100	125	200
Mean	1179.2	1136.0	1057.2
Stdev	102.62	335.57	380.64
AD normality test p-value	0.1975	0.7584	0.2818
p-value	**0.0000**		

Figure 8.19   Bartlett test for transdermal patch adhesiveness example.

has a standard deviation of 335.6 g/system, and adhesive C has a standard deviation of 380.6 g/system. Because the averages for the three adhesives are about the same (1179.2 for adhesive A, 1136.0 for adhesive B, and 1057.2 for adhesive C), the adhesive with the lower variation must be selected. As in the example where the F-test was used, adhesive A must be the chosen one.

Another graph will be developed for this analysis: the histogram and descriptive statistics. The results for each of the three adhesives are presented in Figure 8.20. The Anderson-Darling normality test shows that the

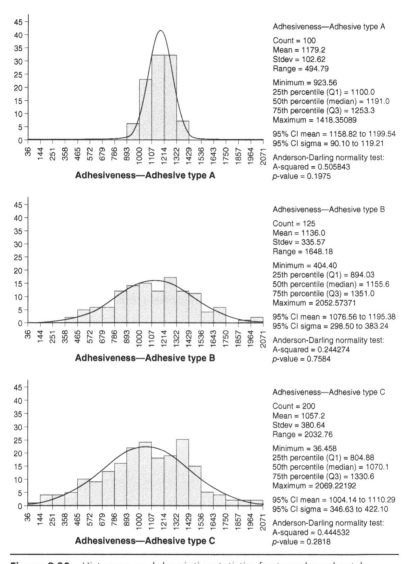

Figure 8.20 Histogram and descriptive statistics for transdermal patch adhesiveness example.

normality hypothesis cannot be rejected for any adhesive type. Furthermore, a look at the minimum values shows that adhesive C will not be complying with the lower specification limit of 300 g/system because there are values below that lower specification limit.

8.4.3 Levene Test

The *F*-test and Bartlett test are used when the data fit a normal distribution. When the data do not fit a normal distribution, we can perform the Levene test. As opposed to the *F*-test and Bartlett test, the Levene test applies for the comparison of two or more variances. Let us illustrate the use of the Levene test through an example:

A company wants to evaluate the time it takes analysts to perform a certain laboratory test and find out why there is so much variation in the time it takes the various shifts to complete the test. To start the analysis, the company records how much time it takes each analyst to perform the laboratory test (in hours). Then, the data are segregated by shift. The box plots for the three shifts are presented in Figure 8.21.

Notice in Figure 8.21 that although shift 2 takes a longer time to complete the test, the analysts in that shift are more consistent; in other words, their variability is much less than the variability of shift 1 and shift 3. Furthermore, there are three outliers showing shorter times than the rest of shift 2.

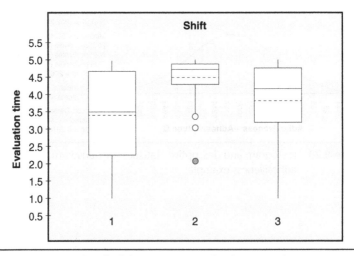

Figure 8.21 Box plots for laboratory test evaluation example.

Levene test for equal variance: evaluation time (Use with nonnormal data)			
Test information H_0: Variance 1 = Variance 2 = . . . = Variance k H_a: At least one pair Variance $i \neq$ Variance j			
Shift	**1**	**2**	**3**
Count	31	42	27
Mean	3.41	4.52	3.82
Median	3.50	4.75	4.18
Stdev	1.304	0.618	1.092
AD normality test p-value	**0.0021**	**0.0000**	**0.0190**
p-value	**0.0000**		

Figure 8.22 Levene test for laboratory test evaluation example.

Figure 8.22 shows the Anderson-Darling normality test results in terms of their p-values: 0.0021 for shift 1, 0.0000 for shift 2, and 0.0190 for shift 3. Based on these results, we can conclude that none of the data sets fits the normal distribution. So, as mentioned earlier, we cannot use the F-test or Bartlett test to analyze the variances. Instead, we need to use the Levene test to compare the variances. Figure 8.22 shows the standard deviations for the three shifts: 1.304 hours for shift 1, 0.618 hours for shift 2, and 1.092 hours for shift 3.

In the Levene test, the null hypothesis is that there is not a significant difference in the variances, and the alternate hypothesis is that at least one variance is significantly different. Taking a look at the p-value for that test (0.0000), we can conclude that at least one variance is significantly different. Analyzing the results, it is evident that the variation in shift 2 is much lower than the variation in shift 1 and shift 3. So, the company will need to identify the causes of the smaller variation in that shift as compared with the other two shifts. Then, those improvements to reduce variability could be extended to the other shifts.

8.5 SUMMARY

Whenever we want to make improvements in our processes, some of the most useful tests for analyzing different alternatives are the hypothesis tests. Using these tools, several groups can be compared in terms of averages, medians, variances, and so on. In a hypothesis test, we want to determine whether the observed difference between groups is due to the random variation of the process or if that difference is caused by a change in the process.

Before performing a hypothesis test, we need to address the normality of the data: If data fit a normal distribution, the tests to be performed are called *parametric* tests; if data do not fit a normal distribution, the tests are called *nonparametric* tests. The parametric tests for central tendency use the *average*, while the nonparametric tests for central tendency use the *median*. When comparing central tendency, we need to select the test based on the number of groups we want to compare: a group against a standard, or a group against another group or more than two groups.

In a similar way, when comparing variances, we need to determine if we want to compare one variance versus another or more than two variances. Also, when comparing variances, we need to assess normality to determine the most appropriate test. The results of the hypothesis tests will be used in subsequent analyses.

9

Regression Analysis

9.1 OVERVIEW

Regression analysis is a statistical technique for estimating the relationships between variables. The focus is on the relationship between a *dependent* variable (also known as *output* or *y*) and one or more *independent* variables (also known as *input* or *x*). Specifically, regression analysis helps us to understand how the typical value of the dependent variable changes when any one of the independent variables is changed while the other independent variables are held fixed. A *scatter plot* shows the relationship between two variables in a process. Dots representing data points are scattered on the diagram. The extent to which the dots cluster together in a line across the diagram shows the strength with which the two factors are correlated. If the variables are correlated, when one changes, the other probably also changes. Dots that look like they are trying to form a line are strongly correlated. Figure 9.1 shows the different types of linear relationships that can be observed in a process.

Regression analysis is widely used for prediction and forecasting. It is also used to understand which of the independent variables are correlated to the dependent variable and to explore the type of relationship. In some cases, regression analysis can be used to infer causal relationships between the independent and dependent variables. However, this can lead to false relationships, so caution is advisable. In other words, correlation does not imply causation. For example, although a scatter plot could show a positive correlation between the amount of rainfall in a country and the amount of wealth in that country, there is no causation between those two variables.

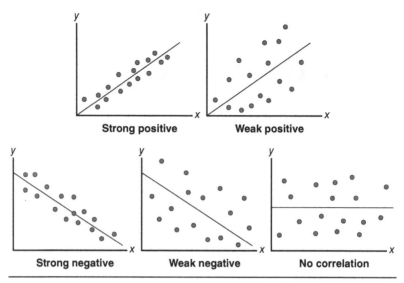

Figure 9.1 Types of correlation.

9.2 LEAST SQUARES METHOD

The regression equation is determined by a procedure that minimizes the total squared distance of *all* points from the regression line. This procedure is called the *least squares method*. It finds the line where the squared vertical distance from each data point to the regression line (called *residuals*) is as small as possible. Regression uses the least squares method to determine the "best fitting line." In other words, the principle of least squares is, *Choose, as the best fitting line, the line that minimizes the sum of squares of the deviations of the observed values of Y from the predicted values.* Figure 9.2 shows the concept behind the least squares method.

9.3 REGRESSION METRICS

Once the "best" regression line is obtained, we need to analyze some metrics to determine how appropriate the regression model is. Two of the metrics are the *correlation coefficient* and the *determination coefficient*.

The correlation coefficient (*r*) is a number that ranges from −1 to +1. This metric provides two important aspects of the regression model: *magnitude* and *slope direction*. For instance, when the correlation coefficient

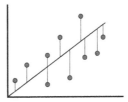

Figure 9.2   The least squares method.

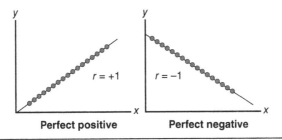

Figure 9.3   Perfect correlation.

is equal to −1, all the data points fall in a straight, decreasing line. This is also called a *perfect negative correlation*. When the correlation coefficient is equal to +1, all the data points fall in a straight, increasing line. This is also called a *perfect positive correlation*. Figure 9.3 illustrates this concept.

When the data points begin to scatter away from the straight line, the correlation coefficient starts to move away from −1 or +1. That is, they move from those extreme values toward zero. A correlation coefficient of zero means there is no linear correlation. In summary, the closer the value to either −1 or +1, the stronger the correlation; the closer to zero, the weaker the correlation. Figure 9.4 shows this concept.

The other metric is called the *determination coefficient*. It is often referred to as r^2 or R^2. It is basically the square of the correlation coefficient. Based on the values mentioned above regarding the correlation coefficient (ranging from −1 to +1), the range of values for the determination coefficient goes from zero to +1 (or from 0% to 100%, when expressed as a percentage). But what specific information does the determination coefficient provide? This value represents the percentage of the model defined by the regression equation. That is, if the correlation coefficient is either −1 or +1, then the determination coefficient will be +1 (or 100%). That would represent a perfect correlation. In other words, the regression line equation would represent 100% of the model. Said differently, the independent variable would account for all the variation in the model.

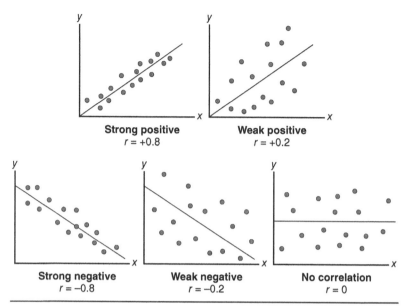

Figure 9.4   Strong and weak correlation.

However, when the correlation coefficient starts to move away from either −1 or +1, there are other independent variables that could be causing the variation. For instance, if the correlation coefficient is −0.8 or +0.8, the determination coefficient will be 0.64, or 64%, which means the regression line equation only accounts for 64% of variation observed in the model. In other words, there is 36% of the variation not explained by the regression equation. In such a case, an approach would be to identify other potential variables that could be affecting the model and include them in a multiple regression model. So, what is an "appropriate" value for the determination coefficient? There is not any specific agreement; however, most references establish that an R^2 higher than 0.80, or 80%, is considered acceptable.

9.4 RESIDUALS ANALYSIS

Once we have determined the best regression line equation and calculated the correlation and determination coefficient, there is another task we need to perform to make certain the calculated regression line equation is statistically valid. This is a task that is rarely performed but is of paramount importance. It is called *residuals analysis*. As mentioned in section 9.2, the residuals are the vertical distance from each data point to the regression line. Said differently, the residuals are the difference between the *expected* value and the *observed* value. The expected value is the value that is represented by the regression line while the observed value is the actual value observed in the process. For the regression analysis to be statistically valid, the residuals must comply with the following assumptions:

- Residuals must be normally distributed.
- Residuals must be in statistical control.
- The average of the residuals must be zero.
- The variation of the residuals must remain constant.

There are many graphical tools that can be used to analyze these assumptions. Most statistical software packages have menus to analyze the residuals. However, those graphs can be prepared individually. For example, to analyze the assumption of normality, we could use a histogram and descriptive statistics, as presented in section 5.2. Also, to verify the assumptions of statistical control, average of zero, and constant variation, a variables control chart (as will be explained in section 11.5) can be used. Figure 9.5 shows the histogram and descriptive statistics for the residuals analysis of a certain process. By looking at both the shape of the histogram and at the *p*-value for the Anderson-Darling normality test (0.8869), it can be seen that the normality assumption for the residuals remains valid.

To verify the other three assumptions, an individuals control chart of the residuals is developed. As can be seen in Figure 9.6, all data points (residuals) are within the control limits; that is, residuals are in statistical control. Also note that the average of the residuals (the centerline of Figure 9.6) is zero. The control chart also shows that variation has remained

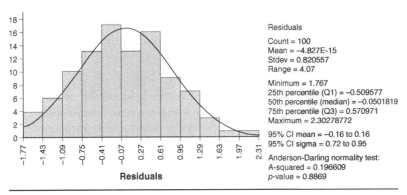

Figure 9.5 Histogram and descriptive statistics for residuals analysis.

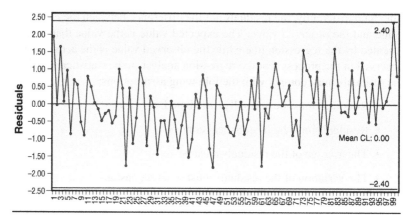

Figure 9.6   Individual control chart for residuals analysis.

constant over time (i.e., it does not show a pattern of increasing or decreasing over time).

Now that we know the basics of regression analysis, let us explore two types of regression analysis: simple linear regression and multiple linear regression.

9.5 SIMPLE LINEAR REGRESSION

In *simple linear regression*, we analyze the relationship between one independent variable and one dependent variable. The equation for the simple linear regression model is:

$$y = \beta_0 + \beta_1 x + \varepsilon$$

where y is the dependent variable, x is the independent variable, β_0 is the y-intercept, and β_1 is the slope. There is also an error term, defined by ε. Let us explain the concept with an example:

A call center for a mobile service provider wants to analyze which variables have the most significant impact on customer satisfaction. So, after a customer complaint was received at the call center and finally resolved, certain information was requested from the complainant through a survey. The information collected included distance of complainant from call center, ease of communications, and responsiveness to call. To simplify the analysis, the customer service department began by analyzing only one variable: ease of communications. To analyze this variable, a Likert scale ranging from 1 to 5 was developed, with 1 meaning very difficult to communicate and 5 meaning very easy to communicate. Also, a customer satisfaction index was developed using the same scale, with a 1 meaning very unsatisfied and 5 meaning very satisfied. Ratings for each day were collected and averaged. Figure 9.7 shows the scatter plot for those averages of the responses for the past 100 days.

It can be seen that as ease of communications increases, the customer satisfaction index also increases; that is, there is a positive relationship between ease of communications and customer satisfaction index. Although there seems to be a positive relationship between these two variables, it does not seem to be too strong because the data points are too scattered around the regression line. So, a regression analysis was performed using statistical software. Figure 9.8 shows the results of this regression analysis.

The regression equation calculated by the analysis was:

Customer satisfaction index = (1.403) + (0.639981)
× Ease of communications

The slope (0.639981) demonstrates there is a positive relationship between ease of communications and customer satisfaction index. However, is that a strong relationship or a weak relationship? Taking a look at

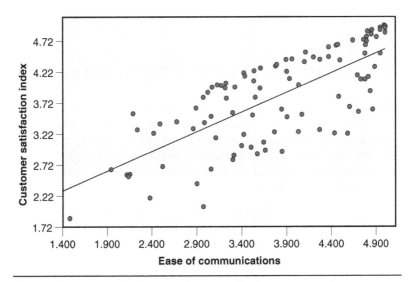

Figure 9.7 Scatter plot for ease of communications versus customer satisfaction index.

Simple regression model: Customer satisfaction index = (1.403) + (0.639981) × Ease of communications				
Model summary:				
R-squared	55.56%			
Parameter estimates:				
Predictor term	**Coefficient**	**SE coefficient**	**T**	**P**
Constant	1.403	0.222942	6.291	**0.0000**
Ease of communications	0.639981	0.057813498	11.070	**0.0000**

Figure 9.8   Regression analysis for ease of communications versus customer satisfaction index.

the R^2 (*R*-squared) value, it is 55.56%, or 0.5556. Taking the square root of that value gives us the value of the correlation coefficient, which is 0.745. Not a bad value. It seems there is a moderate relationship between ease of communications and customer satisfaction index. However, returning to the R^2 value, it is only 55.56%. What does that mean?

Recall from section 9.3 that an R^2 value higher than 80% is considered acceptable. In this example, the obtained R^2 value means that only 55.56% of the variation observed in the regression model is explained by the simple linear regression equation; that is, there is another 44.44% of the observed variation that is explained by some other factors not considered in our regression model. So, let us turn our attention to multiple linear regression.

9.6 MULTIPLE LINEAR REGRESSION

As mentioned in section 9.3, whenever the simple linear regression model provides a low value for the determination coefficient (e.g., $R^2 < 80\%$), that means there are other variables not considered that are affecting the model. In such a case, we would need to identify which other variables could be affecting the model. The *multiple linear regression* model can be explained by the following formula:

$$y = \beta_0 + \beta_1 x_1 + \beta_2 x_2 + \beta_3 x_3 + \ldots + \beta_n x_n + \varepsilon$$

where y is the dependent variable, the x's (x_1, x_2, x_3, and so on) are the independent variables, β_0 is the y-intercept, and the other β's (β_1, β_2, β_3, and so on) are the slopes for each of the independent variables. There is also an error term, defined by ε. Let us explain the concept with an example:

Because the customer service managers of the call center in the previous example realized that other variables not considered in the simple regression model might be affecting the analysis, they decided to include other factors, such as distance from call center (expressed in miles), number of complaints received during the day, and responsiveness to calls. For the last one (responsiveness to calls) the same scale from 1 to 5 was used, 1 meaning poor responsiveness and 5 meaning excellent responsiveness. The results of the multiple linear regression analysis are presented in Figure 9.9.

Notice that R^2 value has increased from 55.56% to 90.10%. Now, 90.10% of the variation observed in the model is explained by the following multiple regression equation:

$$\text{Customer satisfaction index} = (0.408903) + (0.000293)$$
$$\times \text{Distance from call center}$$
$$+ (0.001892) \times \text{Number of complaints}$$
$$\text{received} + (0.433466) \times \text{Responsiveness to}$$
$$\text{calls} + (0.430775) \times \text{Ease of communications}$$

But are all the factors significant for the regression equation? In Appendix C, the hypothesis test for regression analysis is presented. The null and alternate hypotheses are:

H_0: Data are not correlated
H_a: Data are correlated

Multiple regression model: Customer satisfaction index = (0.408903) + (0.000293) × Distance from call center + (0.001892) × Number of complaints received + (0.433466) × Responsiveness to calls + (0.430775) × Ease of communications

Model summary:

R-squared	90.10%

Parameter estimates:

Predictor term	Coefficient	SE coefficient	T	P
Constant	0.408903	0.232912	1.756	0.0824
Distance from call center	0.000293	0.002507031	0.116701	0.9073
Number of complaints received	0.001892	0.004489271	0.421513	0.6743
Responsiveness to calls	0.433466	0.02450545	17.689	**0.0000**
Ease of communications	0.430775	0.030548301	14.101	**0.0000**

Figure 9.9   Four-factor multiple regression analysis for customer satisfaction index.

Multiple regression model: Customer satisfaction index = 0.493463 + (0.435673) × Responsiveness to calls + (0.433346) × Ease of communications				
Model summary:				
R-squared		90.08%		
Parameter estimates:				
Predictor term	**Coefficient**	**SE coefficient**	**T**	**P**
Constant	0.493463	0.116857	4.223	0.0001
Responsiveness to calls	0.435673	0.023710993	18.374	**0.0000**
Ease of communications	0.433346	0.029667131	14.607	**0.0000**

Figure 9.10   Two-factor multiple regression analysis for customer satisfaction index.

Appendix C shows that when the obtained *p*-value is lower than a significance level (α), the null hypothesis will be rejected and the alternate hypothesis will be accepted. So, in order to conclude that input variable (x) is related to the output variable (y), we must obtain a *p*-value lower than the significance level (α). Considering that $\alpha = 0.05$, all the input variables with a *p*-value lower than 0.05 will be considered significant; that is, those input variables are related to the output variables. Taking another look at Figure 9.9, we can see that only *Responsiveness to calls* and *Ease of communications* have *p*-values lower than 0.05. We can conclude those two input variables are related to the output variable, *Customer satisfaction index*. So, we will rule out the other two variables and run the analysis again. Figure 9.10 shows the results.

Notice that R^2 value has only decreased from 90.10% to 90.08%. Now, 90.08% of the observed variation in the model is explained by the following multiple regression equation:

Customer satisfaction index = (0.493463) + (0.435673)
× Responsiveness to calls + (0.433346)
× Ease of communications

This regression equation can be used to predict the value of the customer satisfaction index based on the values of *Responsiveness to calls* and *Ease of communications*. Before proceeding further, an important point has to be reinforced here. We had discarded the factors *Distance from call center* and *Number of complaints received* because, when considered individually, they are not statistically significant. However, at this time we do not know if the *interaction* of those factors with other factors can be statistically significant. A deeper study, including a design of experiments (DOE), could be used to learn more about the main effects and their interactions.

9.7 SUMMARY

The regression analysis provides useful information for the design of experiments, which will be explained in the next chapter. Regression can assist in the determination of which input variables have an impact on the output variables. It may also help us understand the kind of relationship between the input variables and output variables (positive correlation or negative correlation), and the magnitude of that relationship (strong or weak). One weakness of regression analysis is that it is done with already collected data. In that sense, there could be some uncontrollable factors affecting the results. For this reason, the design of experiments will be presented as a systematic tool for identifying the sources of process variability using a controlled environment.

10

Design of Experiments

10.1 OVERVIEW

In industry, designed experiments can be used to systematically investigate the process or product variables that influence product quality. After you identify the process conditions and product components that influence product quality, you can direct improvement efforts to enhance a product's manufacturability, reliability, quality, and field performance. Because resources are limited, it is very important to get the most information from each experiment you perform. Well-designed experiments can produce significantly more information and often require fewer runs than haphazard or unplanned experiments. In addition, a well-designed experiment will ensure that you can evaluate the effects that you have identified as important.

There are many approaches to learn about a process: on-site observation, empirical data analysis, classical experiments, and statistical designed experiments, among others. Classical experiments focus on OFAT (one factor at a time) at two or three levels and try to hold everything else constant ("blocked"), which is impossible to do in a complicated process. The classical approach of changing one variable at a time has many shortcomings:

- Too many experiments are necessary to study the effects of all the input factors.

- The optimum combination of all the variables may never be revealed.

- The interaction between factors (the behavior of one factor being dependent on the level of another factor) cannot be determined.

When a statistical designed experiment is properly constructed, it can focus on a wide range of key input factors or variables and will determine the optimum levels of each of the factors. There are some benefits to using statistical *design of experiments* (DOE):

- Many factors can be evaluated simultaneously.

- One can look quickly at a process with relatively few experiments.

- If some (noise) factors cannot be controlled, other input factors can be controlled.

- In-depth, statistical knowledge is not necessary to get a big benefit.

- Quality can be improved without cost increase.

- In many cases, tremendous cost savings can be achieved.

Factorial designs allow for the simultaneous study of the effects that several factors may have on a process. When performing an experiment, varying the levels of the factors simultaneously rather than one at a time is efficient in terms of time and cost and allows for the study of interactions between factors. Interactions are the driving force in many processes. Without the use of factorial experiments, important interactions may remain undetected.

10.2 DESIGN OF EXPERIMENTS TERMINOLOGY

When dealing with DOE, some specific words come into play. Table 10.1 shows some of the most-used words in DOE, along with their counterparts in our day-to-day conversations about statistical tools.

Table 10.1 Design of experiments terminology.

Common term	Design of experiments term
Input (x)	Factor
Output (y)	Response
Setting	Level
Result	Effect
Uncontrollable input	Noise
Combination of inputs and settings	Treatment, run

A DOE can be defined as a systematic way to treat the factors at certain levels in order to evaluate the effect on the response variable—or, in layman's terminology, to test the different combinations of inputs and settings in order to evaluate the result on the output variable.

In DOE there is a term called "noise." It refers specifically to an input that cannot be controlled or is too difficult or costly to control. Some examples might be humidity, raw material quality, operators, and so on. As will be explained later, in a *full factorial experiment*, all the factors are tested at all the levels. Traditionally, we select two levels for each factor (usually called "low" level and "high" level). This means that we need to specify certain settings that we can control. However, what do we do when we have a factor that cannot be controlled or is too difficult or costly to control? There are many approaches to deal with this. However, one of the most commonly used approaches is "blocking." It essentially means to break our experiment into certain stages (called *blocks*) and run the same treatments on each block. Instead of adding another factor, we analyze the results on each of these blocks and determine if the block is significant or not. Blocking is discussed in detail in section 10.5.

10.3 FULL FACTORIAL EXPERIMENTS

As mentioned in section 10.2, a *full factorial experiment* is one in which we evaluate all the possible combinations of factors and levels. That is, we run all the factors (inputs) at all levels (settings). The most common factorial experiment is called the 2^k, where 2 is the number of levels and k is the number of factors. In this type of experiment, if we have two factors, we will have four combinations; for three factors, we will have eight combinations; for four factors, we will have 16 combinations and so on. The levels are usually identified as "low" and "high," although we can assign numerical or categorical values to them. These levels must be selected in such a way that they are not too close together or too far apart. Too close is not good because we might not see a change in the response variable when one does exist; too far is not good because we might be experiencing unwanted nonlinear relationships.

But with three or more levels, why do we not try to learn more about the process? For example, set the levels to "low," "medium," and "high." The reason is simple: In DOE, it is more desirable to run many small experiments than run too few big experiments. Table 10.2 shows the relationship between the number of factors and levels and their impact on the number of runs for the experiment.

Table 10.2   Relationship between number of levels and factors.

Number of levels	Number of factors	Number of runs
2	2	4
2	3	8
2	4	16
3	2	9
3	3	27
3	4	81

Notice in Table 10.2 that for each additional factor in a 2^k experiment, the number of combinations doubles; however, for each additional factor in a 3^k experiment, the number of combinations triples. Let us analyze the scenario where there are four factors. A 2^k experiment with four factors will require 16 experiments; however, a 3^k experiment with four factors will require 81 experiments. In theory, we could perform five of the 2^k experiments (80 runs) with fewer resources than a single 3^k experiment (81 runs). So, which one do you think will provide the most information with the fewest number of experiments? The 2^k experiment, of course.

10.4 FRACTIONAL FACTORIAL EXPERIMENTS

As mentioned earlier, in a full factorial experiment, we test all the possible combinations of levels and factors. I also mentioned that as the number of factors increases, the number of experiments rises dramatically. So, what alternative do we have when the number of factors in an experiment is high (say, more than five factors)? In this case, we can perform what is called a *fractional factorial experiment.*

In contrast to a full factorial experiment, a fractional factorial experiment minimizes the number of runs. However, we cannot fractionalize the experiment into any arbitrary number of runs. Because in a 2^k full factorial experiment the number of runs doubles with each additional factor, a similar approach will be followed for the fractional factorial. However, in this case, the number of runs will be half for each additional degree of fractionalization. For example, a five-factor full factorial experiment will require

32 runs. However, we could run a half fractional factorial experiment with 16 runs, or a quarter fractional factorial experiment with eight runs, or an eighth fractional factorial experiment with four runs.

It is very important to realize that the degree of fractionalization cannot be set arbitrarily. This is because it would be very tempting to run all fractional factorial experiments with the fewest number of runs possible (e.g., four runs). In fractional factorials there is something called the *resolution*. Technically, the resolution is a measure of the accuracy of the information provided by the experiment. The higher the resolution, the more accurate the information provided. The lower the resolution, the less accurate the information provided. That is, as resolution decreases, the amount of "confounded" effects increases. Confounding occurs when some factors (main factors or interaction factors) are literally aliased with other factors (interaction factors) so that the number of runs can be minimized and we are able to calculate the effects of the main factors. For example, if factor A is confounded with the three-way interaction BCD, then the estimated effect for A is the sum of the effect of A and the effect of BCD. You cannot determine whether a significant effect is because of A, because of BCD, or because of a combination of both. Table 10.3 shows the various resolutions for different degrees of fractionalization.

Imagine that our experiment has six factors at two levels. A full factorial experiment will require a total of 64 runs. However, we could perform a half fractional factorial experiment with 32 runs (resolution VI), a quarter

Table 10.3   Degree of fractionalization versus resolution.

Number of runs	Number of factors													
	2	3	4	5	6	7	8	9	10	11	12	13	14	15
4	Full	III												
8		Full	IV	III	III	III								
16			Full	V	IV	IV	IV	III	III	III	III	III	III	III
32				Full	VI	IV	IV	IV	IV	IV	IV	IV	IV	IV
64					Full	VII	V	IV	IV	IV	IV	IV	IV	IV
128						Full	VIII	VI	V	V	IV	IV	IV	IV

Legend:
Red zone—Resolution III
Yellow zone—Resolution IV
Green zone—Resolution V and above

fractional factorial experiment with 16 runs (resolution IV), or an eighth fractional factorial experiment with eight runs (resolution III). As can be seen in Table 10.3, a full factorial and a half fractional factorial experiment are good options because they are highlighted as *green zone* (resolution V and above). The quarter fractional factorial experiment is highlighted as *yellow zone* (resolution IV), so caution should be exercised because there might be some confounded effects. Finally, the eighth fractional factorial experiment is highlighted in the *red zone* (resolution III), so it is not recommended to use this degree of fractionalization because there are too many confounded effects and the results might hide important information.

10.5 BLOCKING

In the ideal DOE, all factors included in the experiments will be controlled. That is, all factors can be set to determined levels (settings). However, there are certain occasions when a factor cannot be controlled or it could be too costly or too difficult to control. For example, we would probably not be able to control the humidity level in a warehouse, or the variability in a supplied raw material, or the consistency among operators.

In each of these situations, we could try to include the variable as a factor in the experiment. However, how could you guarantee that warehouse humidity is exactly the same throughout the day? Or, how can you be certain that an operator has the same consistency throughout the day? These are only some examples of noncontrollable factors. How do we deal with those factors that cannot be completely controlled or are too costly or difficult to control? An alternative would be to add "blocks" to our experiment.

A *block* is technically a set of conditions that will be replicated at certain times. Instead of adding a factor and analyzing that factor, we are going to add a block and determine whether the block is significant. If the block is not significant, there are no major problems. This means that running our experiment with any of those conditions (e.g., humidity levels, supplied raw material, specific operator, and so on) will not have a significant impact on the response variable. However, if the block becomes significant, we need to determine how that factor (the block) will either be controlled or set to a fixed value. The first option (controlling the factor) might be the most difficult to achieve. So, sometimes when a block becomes significant, the best approach is to determine which of the levels provides the best results. Let me explain with an example:

> During an experiment to determine the hardness of a tablet, a quality engineer found that raw material was an important factor

to consider. The company is currently receiving that raw material from two different suppliers: supplier A and supplier B. Previous experience has shown that raw material is a noncontrollable factor (i.e., raw material is considered a noise factor). Thus, it cannot be included as a factor in the experiment because we are not able to control the levels (settings) of that factor. So, we will include the raw material as a block in our experiment. The other two important factors are *speed* and *compression force*. A two-level factorial experiment with two factors was generated. Table 10.4 shows the eight runs, along with the hardness result for each run. Notice the two blocks that were developed in this experiment: block 1 represents the raw material for supplier A, and block 2 represents the raw material for supplier B.

Figure 10.1 shows the results when the experiment was analyzed using statistical software. Notice that the blocks are not significant because they have a high p-value (0.638). More on this will be presented in section 10.8. From this experiment, we can conclude that raw material (i.e., which supplier to use) does not have an impact on the tablet hardness. But what if the p-value was very small (e.g., lower than 0.05)? In that case, raw material would be considered an important factor because, based on which supplier we use, the tablet hardness would be different. Should we include this factor in our experiment? It depends. Remember that levels in the experiment must be controllable. In the current situation, if raw material is not controllable, my opinion would be to use only raw material from the supplier that provides the best quality. A two-sample t-test can be used to compare the means of the hardness (subject to normality of the data) and an F-test could be used to compare the variances of the hardness (again, subject to normality of data).

10.6 REPETITION AND REPLICATION

Very often when we are designing an experiment, we hear the words *repetition* and *replication*. They might seem like they are the same thing; however, each of these terms represents something different. Most people tend to use them interchangeably because the terms are somewhat confusing. Let me explain, in practical terms, what each of these terms represents.

When we are doing *repetitions* in DOE, we are really not repeating anything. What we are doing is just taking more than one sample from each run. That is, for each combination of factor and level, we obtain more than one result. What is the advantage? With more than one datum, we can calcu-

Table 10.4   Data table for blocking experiment.

Blocks	A: Machine speed	B: Compression force	Hardness
1	1000	20	5
1	3000	20	8
1	1000	40	4
1	3000	40	10
2	1000	20	6
2	3000	20	9
2	1000	40	4
2	3000	40	9

Term	Coefficient	SE coefficient	T	P
Constant	6.750	0.339	19.941	**0.000**
A: Machine speed	2.125	0.239	8.878	**0.003**
B: Compression force	−0.125	0.239	−0.522	0.638
AB	0.625	0.239	2.611	0.080
Blocks—2	0.250	0.479	0.522	0.638

Figure 10.1   Results for blocking experiment.

late descriptive statistics such as average, median, range, standard deviation, and so on. Out of these descriptive statistics, the measures of dispersion (range, standard deviation, and variance) play an important role. Specifically, from each run we can calculate what is called *short-term variability*. The logic is that if we are keeping things constant within a run, why would we see variability in the results? The answer is simple: Because of the inherent variation in the process itself *at that moment*. Table 10.5 shows a *repeated* experiment.

Notice that for each run, two samples were taken. We could use that information to calculate the measures of central tendency (average, median, and so on) and the measures of dispersion (range, standard deviation, and so on). Then, our experiment would not only be focused on hitting a target (e.g., the nominal value of the specification), but also on reducing the variation (i.e., obtaining the optimal combination of factor and level that provides the smallest variation possible).

Table 10.5   Repetition in DOE.

A: Machine speed	B: Compression force	Hardness 1	Hardness 2
1000	20	5	5
3000	20	8	7
1000	40	4	4
3000	40	10	11

In contrast, when we change the conditions between each run, we will be able to calculate the *long-term variability*. When we do this, we are using *replications* within our experiment. In a replicated experiment, we are capturing the process variation in the long run. That is, we are also considering the effect of some factors that were not included in our experiment. What is the logic? If we run a certain combination of factor and level at some point we might expect that the same combination could be run at any other time and the result would be the same or very similar. If that presumption does not hold true, then there might be some other factors not considered that are influencing the response variable. In that case, we would need to extend our experiment to include such factors. Table 10.6 shows an example of a *replicated* experiment.

So, what is the best approach? To consider *both repetition and replication* in our experiment. Table 10.7 shows an example where we consider both.

Notice that *repetition* can be observed for each run. Two tablets were collected for each combination of factor and level. As mentioned, short-term variability can be calculated from this approach. *Replication* can be observed for run #1 and #5 (1000, 20), run #2 and #6 (3000, 20), run #3 and #7 (1000, 40), and run #4 and #8 (3000, 40). Long-term variability can then be calculated.

But what is the practical application of considering short-term and long-term variability in our experiments? One of the most common errors in experimental design is to focus just on hitting the target regardless of the variation. The best experiment would consider both. Let us imagine the nominal value is 10 kp for the average tablet hardness, with a tolerance from 6 to 14 kp. Suppose that one combination of factor and level resulted in an average hardness of 10 kp and a standard deviation of 1.0 kp. This means that 99.73% of the data will fall between 7 and 13 kp. However, there was another combination that resulted in an average hardness of 11 kp and a standard deviation of 0.5 kp. This would mean that 99.73% of the data will

Table 10.6 Replication in DOE.

A: Machine speed	B: Compression force	Hardness 1
1000	20	5
3000	20	8
1000	40	4
3000	40	10
1000	20	6
3000	20	9
1000	40	4
3000	40	9

Table 10.7 Repetition and replication in DOE.

A: Machine speed	B: Compression force	Hardness 1	Hardness 2
1000	20	5	5
3000	20	8	7
1000	40	4	4
3000	40	10	11
1000	20	6	5
3000	20	9	9
1000	40	4	4
3000	40	9	10

fall between 9.5 and 12.5 kp. Which combination of factor and level would provide the more consistent product? The second combination (9.5 to 12.5 kp), of course. However, if we had just focused on the central tendency, we would have chosen the first combination.

Another way to see the impact of just focusing on central tendency alone is to calculate the capability indices for both scenarios. For the first combination (average = 10 kp, standard deviation = 1.0 kp), C_p will be 1.33 and C_{pk} also 1.33. This is not so bad, as we already mentioned in section 7.3. But what would be the capability indices for the second combination (average = 11 kp, standard deviation = 0.5 kp)? The answer is $C_p = 2.67$ and $C_{pk} = 2.00$. Again, which combination provides the best result? The one that is somewhat off-target but with the smallest variation. In summary, the next time you perform a DOE, remember to consider descriptive statistics measures for both central tendency and dispersion.

10.7 EXPERIMENTAL STRATEGY

Sections 10.3 and 10.4 presented the concepts of full factorial and fractional factorial experiments, respectively, and explained the differences between them. Advantages and limitations of each were also explained. But when is it more appropriate to use each one of these types of experiments? The answer must be related to the amount of knowledge we have about the process we want to study.

When the process knowledge is low (because it is a new process or it has not been thoroughly studied), the best approach is to start with a fractional factorial experiment. In this way, we can experiment with many variables and learn more about their effect on the response variable(s). Just remember that experimentation is sequential; that is, we will apply the knowledge acquired in each experiment to subsequent experiments. Once our process knowledge becomes better, we can then start using full factorial experiments. But remember, one limitation with full factorial experiments is that the number of experiments becomes larger as the number of factors increases. So, our first full factorial experiments must not be replicated. At this point, we still want to keep the number of runs as low as possible.

Once we are certain we have included the appropriate factors in our experiment (at the appropriate levels), we would like to add replications to our experiments. In this way, long-term variability will be accounted for. A few full factorial *replicated* experiments will help us make certain we have considered all the significant factors and levels. Finally, a few validation runs would be appropriate once we have found the factors and levels that optimize our response variable(s). The following diagram shows the approach:

Fractional factorial (unreplicated) → Full factorial (unreplicated)
→ Full factorial (replicated) → Validation runs

Following the approach outlined above, we can be confident that we are using the available resources in the most efficient way and we are continuously expanding our process knowledge.

10.8 DESIGN OF EXPERIMENTS EXAMPLE: TWO LEVELS, TWO FACTORS

Let me explain the concept of a two-level, two-factor full factorial experiment with an example:

A pharmaceutical company has been performing some experiments in order to optimize the hardness of a tablet. The specification for the tablet hardness is 10 ± 0.5 kp. So far, the company has acquired much process knowledge through previous experimentation. During this process, the company has performed fractional factorial and unreplicated full factorial experiments. The company has also experimented with center points and blocks to rule out curvature and noise factors, respectively. At this point, a replicated full factorial experiment will be performed.

The two factors that have been demonstrated to be more significant throughout all the experimentation stages in the compression process are *machine speed* and *compression force*. The levels to test in this experiment will be 1000 and 3000 revolutions per minute (rpm) for the machine speed and 20 and 40 kilonewtons (kN) for the compression force. A replicated two-level, two-factor experiment was developed. The results are presented in Table 10.8.

Using statistical software, the results were analyzed. Figure 10.2 shows the main effects plots for this experiment. How is the main effects plot analyzed? On the *x*-axis, you will find the two levels for each factor (1000 and 3000 rpm for machine speed, and 20 and 40 kN for compression force). On the *y*-axis, you will find the average tablet hardness at each level. The steeper the line, the more significant is that factor. When the line is completely flat, it does not matter which level you choose; the average response would be the same. In this example, to achieve an average hardness of about

Table 10.8 Replicated full factorial design example for tablet hardness.

A: Machine speed	B: Compression force	Tablet hardness
3000	20	8.8
1000	20	9.2
3000	20	8.1
1000	40	9.1
3000	40	11.6
1000	20	8.7
1000	40	8.3
3000	40	11.0

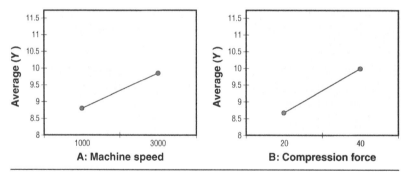

Figure 10.2 Main effects plots for tablet hardness example.

10.0 kp, the machine speed should be set at 3000 rpm and the compression force at 40 kN.

But is the interaction between the machine speed and compression force significant? That is, would selecting a different machine speed or compression force cause a difference in the response variable? Figure 10.3 shows the interaction plots for the experiment.

How will we determine the strength of the interaction between machine speed and compression force? If the lines are completely perpendicular, there is a strong interaction; if the lines are completely parallel, there is no inter-action. In this example, the lines are neither completely perpendicular nor

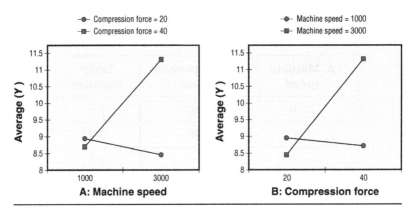

Figure 10.3   Interaction plots for tablet hardness example.

Term	Coefficient	T	P
Constant	9.350	56.706	**0.0000**
A: Machine speed	0.525	3.184	**0.0334**
B: Compression force	0.650	3.942	**0.0169**
AB	0.775	4.700	**0.0093**

Figure 10.4   Factorial design analysis for table hardness example.

completely parallel. However, the lines are closer to perpendicular than parallel, so we can conclude that there is a strong interaction between machine speed and compression force.

As mentioned earlier when analyzing the main effects plots, by setting the machine speed to 3000 rpm and the compression force to 40 kN, we achieve an average hardness of about 10 kp, which is the nominal value. But what if, leaving machine speed at 3000 rpm, we decide to set compression force to 20 kN? The plot on the left side of Figure 10.3 shows that average hardness would drop significantly. The same will happen if we set the compression force at 40 kN but set the machine speed at 1000 rpm, as shown on the right side of Figure 10.3.

We can conclude that both the main effects factors and the interaction factors seem to be significant, based on these plots. However, as mentioned earlier, we cannot rely only on the graphs to make a conclusion about the significance of the main effects and interaction factors. So, we need to study the analytical portion of the experiment. Figure 10.4 shows the results obtained using statistical software.

Based on the results in Figure 10.4, at a significance level of 0.05 ($\alpha = 0.05$), we can conclude that both main effects (machine speed and compression force) and the interaction of those effects are significant. More information about when to reject and fail to reject H_0 is provided in Appendix C for the most commonly used hypothesis tests.

10.9 SUMMARY

So far, we have been analyzing data that were previously collected. From that data, different evaluations have been performed: practical, graphical, and analytical. The tools studied so far have assisted us to get a better understanding of our processes. The next step is to use that knowledge to find the inputs and settings that will optimize the results, through an approach called design of experiments (DOE).

The type of DOE to perform will depend on the process knowledge. When process knowledge is low, we will start experimenting with fractional factorials. Then, as process knowledge becomes better, we will experiment with full factorials. When using fractional factorials, the level of fractionalization is an important element to consider. We select the level of fractionalization based on the resolution provided by each alternative. Resolution III must never be run; resolution IV experiments must be used with caution; resolution V and above are recommended.

When performing full factorial experiments, we could start with unreplicated experiments. Then, as process knowledge becomes better, we could add replicates in order to calculate the long-term variability. Also, repetitions could be added in order to calculate the short-term variability. Experimentation must not focus only on achieving a target, but also on reducing variation.

11
Control Charts

11.1 OVERVIEW

In Chapter 3, the concept of process variation was introduced. The assumption is that all processes are subject to some kind of variation. Two types of variation were defined: *common-cause* variation and *special-cause* variation. Common-cause variation is always present in every process because no process is perfect. Common-cause variation is inherent in every process. In contrast, special-cause variation is not always present in every process. This type of variation is caused by assignable events—that is, by certain things that have a significant impact on the process.

In Chapter 5 some graphical tools for analyzing data were presented. Tools like the histogram, box plot, dot plot, and Pareto diagram (among others) were presented and discussed. The major disadvantage of those tools is that they represent the data in a static way. For example, a histogram can help us describe the data in terms of central tendency, dispersion, and shape. However, the histogram does not tell us anything about each individual value in terms of *time*. How could we obtain the advantages of learning about central tendency, dispersion, and shape along with the advantages of learning how the process behaves over time? Very simple: by using a *control chart*.

Recall from Chapter 7 there is something we call the *process spread*, also known as the *voice of the process*. The process spread is quantified by the standard deviation, σ. Specifically, it is defined by the interval of $\pm 3\sigma$ from the mean. As mentioned in section 4.5, in a normal distribution about 99.73% of the data is expected to fall within $\pm 3\sigma$ from the mean. So, we will use that fact in order to calculate what are called *control limits*. In a control chart, the control limits define the region where the common causes of variation are expected to occur. That is, as long as the process is in statistical control, all the points will occur within the control limits defined by the interval of ±3σ from the mean, without any nonrandom pattern, as will be studied later. When we see a point outside of those control limits (or points showing a nonrandom pattern), it indicates some sort of assignable or special cause that needs to be studied and corrected.

11.2 THE RATIONAL SUBGROUP

One of the most important concepts in control charting is the *rational subgroup*. The success of the control chart will depend, in part, on the appropriate selection of the subgroup size. A rational subgroup is just a subset of a group intended to be as homogeneous as possible. In that way, we will be able to compare the variation within each subgroup and compare the variation between subgroups over an extended period. But how do we determine the appropriate subgroup size? That will depend on the process being studied.

Historically, many people use a subgroup size of 5 because it is very convenient for most manufacturing processes. However, a subgroup size of 5 is not always representative of the process. For instance, let us imagine that we are studying a molding process. The mold has 10 cavities. In this case, it would be preferable to select a subgroup size of 10 instead of a subgroup size of 5. Why? Because the subgroup size of 10 will represent the variation of all the parts produced by that mold at a specific time. In that way, a control chart could be developed for that process and take, for instance, the 10 parts produced by the mold at a certain moment every hour. We could then compare the variation within each hour with the variation between hours to see if there are any significant differences in the long run.

11.3 NONRANDOM PATTERNS

As mentioned earlier, if a process is in statistical control, all the points will occur within the control limits without showing any nonrandom pattern. But what are those nonrandom patterns we need to look for? Walter A. Shewhart developed a list of eight nonrandom patterns that might show that something is changing (or has changed) in the process. Every statistical software package has these eight tests, which may be applied individually or in any combination. Figure 11.1 shows the tests for nonrandom patterns to look for when analyzing control charts.

Do we need to adjust our process every time we see one of these eight nonrandom patterns? Not necessarily. Recall from Chapter 7 that being out of control does not necessarily mean producing defective parts. If a process is capable (i.e., the process variation is narrower than the customer specifi-

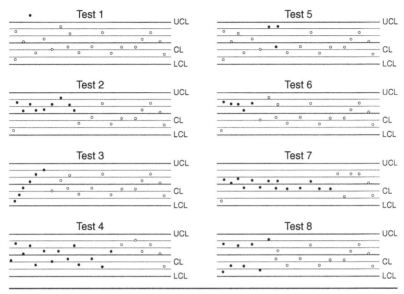

Figure 11.1   Tests for nonrandom patterns in control charting.

cations) and if a point falls outside of the control limits or the chart starts to show a nonrandom pattern, we might still have time to react before the process produces nonconforming parts. So, let me explain some of the possible causes of each of the eight nonrandom patterns to give you an idea of what steps could be taken to adjust the process before it is too late:

- *Test 1—One point more than 3 sigma away from centerline.* This is typically what is called a *special cause.* It is a point produced by an assignable event, some sort of change that caused an extreme variation in the process. Some examples are a contaminated sample, machine failure, change in method, and so on. Using a fishbone diagram could help us identify the potential causes of this kind of situation.

- *Test 2—Nine points in a row on same side of centerline.* This is usually the result of a change in the process centering. Although the process variation might have remained constant, the process has shifted toward one of the control limits. This type of pattern does not necessarily mean that something bad has happened. For instance, we might see a reduction in the average time to complete an investigation after a CAPA certification process if we see this kind of pattern. In contrast, we might see this pattern on a filling process if one or various nozzles become clogged or if the equipment's settings were changed. In any case, this is an indicator that something has happened, and it is a good time to analyze the desirability of such change.

- *Test 3—Six points in a row, all increasing or all decreasing.* This might be an indication of tool wear, machine deterioration, a tired operator, and so on. It does not represent a sudden change in the process but a slight and continuous change in it. This kind of pattern can be easily detected and acted on before it is too late.

- *Test 4—Fourteen points in a row, alternating up and down.* This is an uncommon pattern. This can be caused by overadjustment of the equipment or by manipulation of data. Special attention must be given to data integrity.

- *Test 5—Two out of three points in a row more than 2 sigma away from the centerline (same side).* This pattern might be indicative of a sudden increase in the process variation. It is possible to have some points in this zone from time to time, but two out of three consecutive points is not desirable. The causes of this pattern might be similar to those of test 1; however, in this case the event has not been so significant as to cause an out-of-control point.

- *Test 6—Four out of five points in a row more than 1 sigma away from the centerline (same side).* This might be the beginning of the pattern depicted in test 5. Instead of a sudden increase in variation as in test 5, here we have a slight increase in variation that, if not acted on, can result in out-of-control points.

- *Test 7—Fifteen points in a row within 1 sigma from the centerline (either side).* This pattern indicates that variation has been dramatically reduced, which might lead us to think it is "too good to be true" or to adopt a "do not touch the process" mentality. The main problem here is that a variation reduction has been achieved, but the control limits have not been recalculated. Although a pattern like this might look good, it is not statistically correct. Remember that control limits are based on process variability. If variability decreases, then the control limits must be recalculated and become narrower.

- *Test 8—Eight points in a row more than 1 sigma away from the centerline (either side).* This is a very interesting pattern. It might be indicative of mixtures; that is, combining data from different populations in the same control chart. An example could be to have data from two different machines (each one with a different average) plotted on the same control chart. The solution could be to separate the data for each machine into different control charts. This pattern might also be noticed as a bimodal distribution when a histogram is used to plot the data.

The situations presented above are not intended to cover all the possible causes of variation; they are just some examples of what could be causing each of these nonrandom patterns. The person analyzing the control charts must study the process and find the real causes of such variation. It is also important to note the previous eight rules apply to the variables control charts as they will be defined in section 11.4. However, in the attributes control charts, only test 1 through test 4 will be applicable. That means tests 5 through 8 will not apply to the attributes control charts. If you see one of these patterns in an attributes control chart, they will not be considered nonrandom patterns.

11.4 VARIABLES CONTROL CHARTS AND ATTRIBUTES CONTROL CHARTS

In section 4.2, the different types of data were presented: variable data, attribute data, and locational data. Out of those three types of data, the most used are variable and attribute data. Variable data are *continuous*—data that can be measured. In contrast, attribute data are *discrete*—data that can be counted, categorized, binary, and so on. Depending on the type of data at hand, we could use a different control chart.

One of the most common errors I have seen is the selection of the incorrect control chart. For example, let us say we want to plot the number of complaints received during each month. Because the number of complaints is data that can be counted (discrete), we must use an attributes control chart—in this case, a *c* chart. Many times, I have seen the use of a variables control chart (like an individuals and moving range chart) to plot this type of information. Other common errors I have seen in the use of control charts are:

- Wrong formula used to calculate control limits

- Missing, poor, or erroneous measurements

- Data on charts not current

- Process adjustments have not been noted

- Control limits and average not updated

- Special-cause signals ignored

- Nonrandom patterns not studied

- Specification limits placed on chart instead of control limits

Let me present the different types of variables and attributes control charts available, with some applications for each one.

11.5 VARIABLES CONTROL CHARTS

As mentioned, the variables control charts will be used for continuous data, or data that can be measured. Most parameters in a manufacturing process fit this type of data. The most commonly used variables control charts are the individuals and moving range (IMR) chart, $\bar{X}$ and R chart, and $\bar{X}$ and s chart. Once we determine that our data are continuous, we need to decide which of these charts is the most appropriate. How do we determine which variables control chart to use? It will depend on the subgroup size, as mentioned in section 11.2.

Here are some hints about which chart to use. If the subgroup size is 1, then we will use the IMR chart; if the subgroup size ranges from 2 to 5, then use an $\bar{X}$ and R chart; if the subgroup size is greater than or equal to 6, then use an $\bar{X}$ and s chart. Recall from section 11.2 what is defined as a subgroup and what should be the appropriate subgroup size for each process.

11.5.1 Individuals and Moving Range Chart

Let us suppose that we want to plot the pH of a sample for a certain process. Each individual sample is collected in an individual flask. Since the pH within the flask will be the same (the sample is homogeneous), it does not make any sense to calculate the average of the sample at different locations in the flask. Instead, one sample will be taken from each flask and plotted in an IMR chart. Figure 11.2 shows the data for 100 consecutive samples.

The specification for this process is 7.0 ± 1.0. Although all the points are well within the specification limits, there are three points in the moving range chart that fall outside of the upper control limit. When each individual sample was analyzed, it was found that those out-of-control points were the result of a sudden change in sample #41 (from 7.08 to 6.71), sample #56 (from 7.19 to 6.73), and sample #57 (from 6.73 to 7.15). However, because those individual values are well within the specification limits and those sudden changes did not happen again, it was decided that no adjustments in the process are required. A common error would have been to overreact to

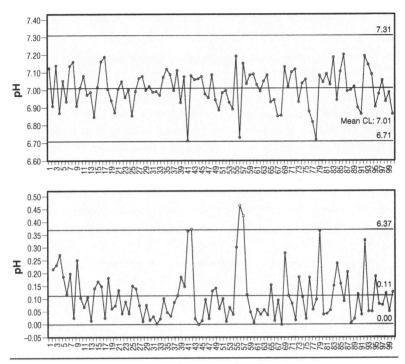

Figure 11.2   Individuals and moving range chart for pH.

those individual values. Overreacting would have caused more points to lie outside of the control limits on both charts.

11.5.2 $\overline{X}$ and R Chart

As mentioned earlier, when the subgroup size varies from 2 to 5, it is recommended to use the $\overline{X}$ and R chart. This is one of the easiest charts to use because both metrics are very simple to calculate. What is the logic behind limiting the use of this chart to subgroup sizes from 2 to 5? Recall that to calculate a range, only two values are needed: the highest value and the lowest value. So, supposing that each value is different, here are the different scenarios for calculating the range:

• For a subgroup size of 2, both values will be used.

• For a subgroup size of 3, two values will be used and one value will be useless.

• For a subgroup size of 4, two values will be used and two values will be useless.

• For a subgroup size of 5, two values will be used and three values will be useless.

For subgroup sizes of 6 and above, the range is not a good measure of process dispersion because too many values will not be used in the calculation. Instead, for such subgroup sizes, the standard deviation (or variance) is recommended because it uses all the individual values. Figure 11.3 shows the $\bar{X}$ and R chart for the tablet weight process of a certain company. Each point in the $\bar{X}$ chart represents the average of the weight of five tablets taken at a certain time while each point in the range chart represents the range of those five tablets. Notice that the process is in statistical control, without any nonrandom pattern.

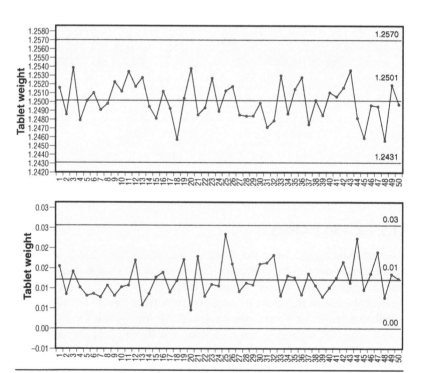

Figure 11.3 $\bar{X}$ and R chart for tablet weight.

11.5.3 $\bar{X}$ and s Chart

Finally, when the subgroup size is 6 and above, it is recommended to use the $\bar{X}$ and s chart. As mentioned, the range is an easy metric to calculate because it is the difference between the largest and the smallest value. However, the standard deviation is somewhat more difficult to calculate. It requires the use of a scientific calculator or a spreadsheet. For that reason, it is seldom used. However, remember that ease of use must not be the main consideration in deciding which chart to use; the main reason must be subgroup size. As subgroup size increases, we are persuaded to use the $\bar{X}$ and s chart instead of the $\bar{X}$ and R chart. Figure 11.4 shows the $\bar{X}$ and s chart for a bottle weight process. The machine fills 10 bottles at a time; that is, it has 10 nozzles. Instead of considering each individual bottle's weight, the company decided to monitor the average weight and variation at certain specific times. So, an $\bar{X}$ and s chart were developed. It can be seen that the process is in statistical control, without any nonrandom pattern.

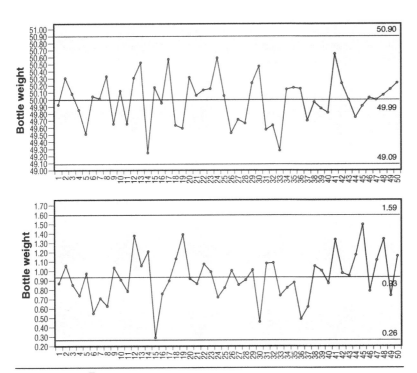

Figure 11.4 $\bar{X}$ and s chart for bottle weight.

11.6 ATTRIBUTES CONTROL CHARTS

If data are discrete, the variables control charts mentioned earlier cannot be used. Instead, we need to use the attributes control charts. The most commonly used attributes control charts are the *p*, *np*, *c*, and *u* charts. How do we determine which attributes control chart to use? It depends on what we want to plot: defectives or defects. A *defective* unit is a unit that has at least one defect. In contrast, a *defect* is any characteristic that does not conform to the specifications. As opposed to the variables control charts, in which two charts are usually plotted on the same page (one chart for central tendency and another for dispersion), in the attributes control charts we only plot one chart at a time. So, what is the difference between the different types of attributes control charts?

The *p* chart and *np* chart are used for *defectives*. Specifically, the *p* chart is used to plot the *percentage defective* while the *np* chart plots the *number of defectives*. On the other hand, the *c* chart and *u* chart are used for *defects*. Particularly, the *c* chart is for *number of defects* while the *u* chart is used for *average number of defects per unit*. I will use Figure 11.5 to illustrate, in a very simplistic way, the difference between the different types of charts using the same data.

Each cylinder represents a single part. There are three subgroups, each of size 3. The "X" symbol within the cylinder represents a single defect. Figure 11.6 shows the calculated values for each of the three subgroups, applied to each of the four types of attributes control charts. So, we can

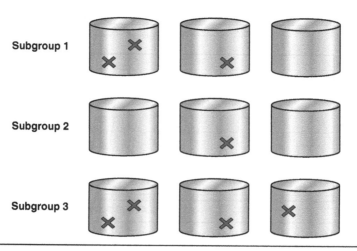

Figure 11.5   Attributes chart example.

	p chart (% defectives)	np chart Number of defectives	c chart Number of defects	u chart Average defects per unit
Subgroup 1	2/3 = 0.67 = 67%	2	3	3/3 = 1.00
Subgroup 2	1/3 = 0.33 = 33%	1	1	1/3 = 0.33
Subgroup 3	3/3 = 1.00 = 100%	3	4	4/3 = 1.33

Figure 11.6 Calculations for attributes charts example.

analyze the same data in different ways by using different control charts. It just depends on which information we want to present.

11.6.1 *p* Chart

The *p* chart is used to analyze the percentage defective in each subgroup. As stated, it does not consider how many defects a unit might have; it considers the whole unit as defective if it has at least one defect. One important consideration for the *p* chart (and for the *u* chart, as will be presented later) is that subgroup size does not have to remain constant. The reason is that what we are plotting is the percentage of defectives, regardless of what the sample size of each subgroup is. For example, if we have one defective in a sample of three units, it will result in 0.33, or 33%, percent defective. On the other hand, if we have three defectives in a sample of nine units, it will also result in 0.33, or 33%, percent defective. Let me explain the use of a *p* chart with an example:

A company is performing an audit of its manufacturing batch records and wants to analyze what percentage of the batch records have any type of error, regardless of the number of errors or type of error. The reason is that any amount or type of error in the

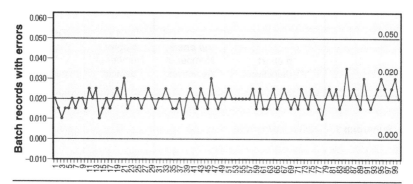

Figure 11.7 *p* chart for percentage of manufacturing batch records with errors.

manufacturing batch record will render the product adulterated. That is, the manufacturing batch record will be considered defective when it has at least one defect. Figure 11.7 shows the information for the records generated during the past year.

As can be seen, the average percentage of manufacturing batch records with errors is 0.02, or 2%. The upper control limit is 5% and the lower control limit is 0%. As long as all the data points are randomly scattered within those limits, there are only common causes of variation acting on the process. When a data point falls above the upper control limit (5%, in this example), then special causes of variation are acting on the process. Please note that being within the control limits (between 0% and 5%, in this example) only means that the process is in statistical control. It does not mean that it is acceptable. For this process parameter (percentage of manufacturing batch records with errors), the goal must be zero. This control chart could be the baseline for a process improvement project about eliminating error in manufacturing batch records.

11.6.2 *np* Chart

As mentioned, the *p* chart is used to plot the percentage of defectives. Sometimes, we do not want to plot the percentage of defectives but the number of defectives. The reason? Mathematically, three defectives out of 10 units is 30%; but 300 defectives out of 1000 units is also 30%. When dealing with products such as pacemakers and antilock brake systems, for example, it is more important that you analyze number of defectives instead of percentage of defectives, especially if you are one of the people receiving the pacemaker or driving the vehicle with the antilock braking system.

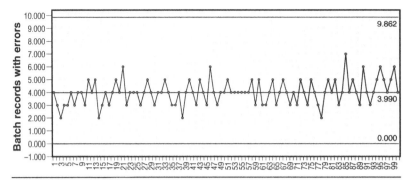

Figure 11.8   *np* chart for number of manufacturing batch records with errors.

One disadvantage of using an *np* chart instead of a *p* chart is that for the *np* chart the subgroup size must remain constant. If the subgroup size varies and we want to plot defectives, then the *p* chart must be used. Let us use the same data from the example of percentage of manufacturing batch records with errors, but this time focus on the number of defectives instead of the percentage defective. Figure 11.8 shows the results for the records produced during the past year.

Recall from the previous example that the control limits just establish the boundaries within which the process is considered to be in statistical control; they do not represent what is considered acceptable. In this example, having fewer than 9.86 defective batch records means that the process is in control. Again, as mentioned earlier, this control chart could be the baseline for a process improvement project about error elimination in manufacturing batch records.

11.6.3 c Chart

In sections 11.6.1 and 11.6.2, I presented the attributes control charts for defectives. Recall that a defective unit is a unit that has at least one defect. Monitoring the *defective* units might be good sometimes, but having knowledge about the *defects* is also important. The *c* chart is used to plot the number of defects in each subgroup. As with the *np* chart, one disadvantage of the *c* chart is that the subgroup size must remain constant. Let us illustrate the application of the *c* chart with an example:

> A company is performing an evaluation of the number of errors found in the manufacturing batch records. Although just one error makes the batch record defective, the team wants to analyze the

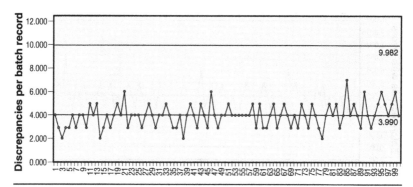

Figure 11.9   *c* chart for number of errors per manufacturing batch record.

number of errors to see the magnitude of the problem and start a project geared toward elimination of errors in the manufacturing batch records. Figure 11.9 shows the *c* chart for number of errors in each batch record. The last 100 batch records were analyzed and plotted in sequential order.

As can be seen in Figure 11.9, as long as the number of errors in each batch record remains between zero and 9.98, the process is in control. But recall from the previous control charts that having errors in the manufacturing batch records is unacceptable. Thus, this control chart can be used to set the baseline and monitor the improvement. The goal is to eventually eliminate the errors in the manufacturing batch records.

11.6.4 *u* Chart

One disadvantage of the *c* chart is that subgroup size must remain constant. But what if the sample size in each subgroup is different? In that case, if we want to plot information about defects, we need to use the *u* chart instead of the *c* chart. Suppose that the company produces so many records that it is almost impossible to analyze all of them. In this case, the company decided instead to take a sample of all records generated each week and plot the data for the average number of errors found each week. A subgroup of 10 records was collected each week. The results are presented in Figure 11.10.

Each data point represents the *average* number of errors per batch record each week. Some records might have more than the average while others might have less than the average. As mentioned earlier, the target must be zero defects. So, this control chart should be used to set a baseline to monitor the improvement over a period of time.

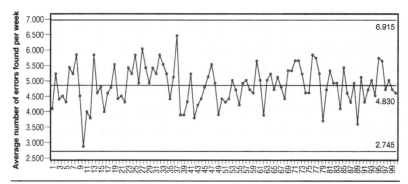

Figure 11.10   *u* chart for average number of errors per batch record per week.

11.7 APPLICATION OF CONTROL CHARTS TO IDENTIFY IMPROVEMENTS IN THE PROCESS

Not only control charts are used to identify special or assignable causes about negative events in our processes, but they can also be used to identify the positive impact of certain process improvement initiatives. The following example can help us understand this point:

A company has been going through certain process improvement projects during the last year. Specifically, about three months ago, a major project to reduce the cycle time in a production line was implemented. Figure 11.11 shows that a downward trend has been observed for approximately the last three months in the cycle time at that production line.

Because the run chart does not provide much information about the common and special causes of variation, an individuals control chart was developed with the same data. When the control limits were calculated and plotted for the data, many special causes were identified in the control chart. Figure 11.12 shows the individuals control chart for cycle time in the production line where the improvements were implemented. One of those special causes identified was having too many points on the same side of the centerline. In fact, this is not a bad situation at all, because precisely what you would want in the improvement project is to reduce the cycle time. Thus, it is expected to have many points below the centerline. However, the

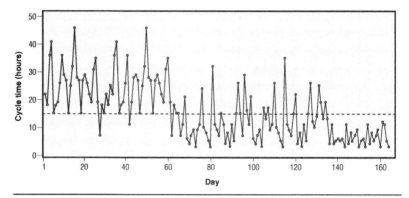

Figure 11.11 Run chart for cycle time in a production line.

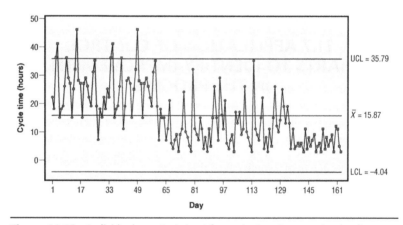

Figure 11.12 Individuals control chart for cycle time in a production line.

main objective was to reduce the average cycle time from approximately 25 hours to less than 10 hours. But the chart is showing that average cycle time after the improvements were implemented is 15.87 hours. What is the main problem with this chart? One mistake is that average and control limits were calculated based on the totality of data, although we already know that the data really come from different time frames when some changes were implemented in the process. So, applying the same control limits for the totality of data is not a good approach.

So, data were analyzed and three regions were identified: the original data before the improvement project was implemented (phase 1), the time frame when some minor improvements were implemented in the process (phase 2), and the time frame when most major improvements to reduce

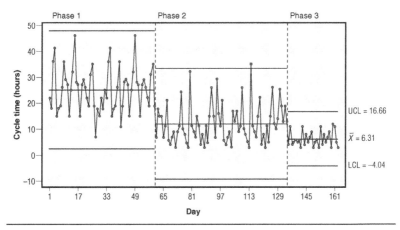

Figure 11.13 Individuals control chart for cycle time by phases of improvements implementation.

the cycle time were finally implemented (phase 3). Thus, the average and the control limits were calculated for each of these three phases and plotted in the same control chart. In Figure 11.13, it can be noticed that, with one exception in phase 2, the process has been in statistical control in each of the three phases. Also, various changes were identified in phase 2 and phase 3. For example, from phase 1 and phase 2, a sudden decrease in the average cycle time (from approximately 25 hours to about 12 hours) was experienced. A slight decrease in the variation was also observed between phase 1 and phase 2. Then, from phase 2 to phase 3, a reduction in average cycle time from about 12 hours to 6.31 hours was noticed. Also, a drastic reduction in the cycle time variation was observed from phase 2 to phase 3.

All of this is very consistent with the time frames when the different improvements were implemented in the process. Thus, it is important to remember that calculating the average and control limits of a data set when the data do not come from a steady process (e.g., some major improvements have been implemented in that process) is not a good idea. Instead, split the data into different groups (or phases) and calculate the average and control limits for each of these phases.

11.8 SUMMARY

Most of the graphical tools studied so far focus on looking at the central tendency, dispersion, and shape of the distribution. They also focus on making comparisons between various groups. However, none of them consider *when* each of the data points were collected. Time is an important consideration in every process. So, plotting the data while the data are being collected can assist us in taking action before any major problem arises.

In previous chapters, I presented different types of data: attribute, variable, and locational. So, when plotting data in a control chart, one of the first issues to consider is which chart to use. For variable data, some of the most commonly used charts are the individuals and moving range (IMR) chart, $\bar{X}$ and R chart, and $\bar{X}$ and s chart. The criterion for selecting the appropriate variables chart will be the subgroup size. On the other hand, for attribute data, the most commonly used charts are the p, np, c, and u charts. The criterion for selecting the appropriate attributes chart will be whether we want to plot data for *defectives* or for *defects*.

When analyzing control charts, one of the aspects to consider is the randomness of the data. There are eight rules for determining whether the process is exhibiting a random pattern or if there are special causes of variation acting on the process. As long as all the data points are within the control limits, without any nonrandom pattern, we can say that the process is in statistical control—or, said differently, only common causes of variation are present. However, when there are data points outside of the control limits, or when some nonrandom pattern is seen, we say that the process is out of statistical control. In this case, we have a combination of common causes and special causes of variation present in the process. Special causes must be identified and eliminated while common causes can be reduced.

Control charts can also be used to identify the impact of certain improvements we have implemented in our processes. Finally, it is important to mention that statistical process control is a requirement for all the tests discussed in this book. So, although control charting was the last tool discussed, it will be one of the first tools to be used prior to any other analysis.

12

Afterword

12.1 OVERVIEW

Throughout the preceding chapters, I have presented several tools to monitor and improve the processes in an organization. The book started by establishing the importance of process monitoring and improvement. The similarities and differences between some regulations and international standards were established. The concept of process variation is an important topic in any manufacturing environment. Thus, understanding the difference between common causes of variation and special causes of variation, along with the basic principles of statistics, must be one of the preliminary topics to include in any quality improvement endeavor. Our process knowledge can be enhanced by the use of graphical tools. Many of these graphical tools, along with specific examples of their application, were presented throughout the book.

It is important to recognize that before starting to collect information, we must make certain that our measurement system is reliable—that is, the measurement process is not adding more variation than the manufacturing process does. Once we have optimized our measurement system, then an assessment of the overall process variation versus the customer specifications must be performed in order to learn how capable our processes are. Then, hypothesis tests can help us understand the statistical differences between various groups, as well as the relationship between the variables that might have an impact on the process. However, no process improvement effort is comprehensive without the use of experimental design; that is, to find which are the factors that impact our key output variables (and which are the appropriate settings of those factors), some sort of systematic experimentation must be executed. It is important to recognize that experimentation is a continual process: With each additional experiment we will gain more process knowledge. Finally, but not less important, we need to continually monitor our processes, not only the process outputs but also the key process inputs. An excellent tool for continuously monitoring processes is the control chart. These charts must be used on a perpetual basis, not just "once a month" or "once a year." Control charts will be one of the cornerstones of any process monitoring and improvement initiative.

12.2 ORDER OF TOOLS

Throughout the book, many process monitoring and improvement tools are presented. I have made an attempt to present the tools in the specific order in which they must be implemented. Most of the monitoring and improvement tools have been explained throughout the book; others have not been explained but can be found in many quality tools textbooks. What follows are, based on my experience, some of the recommended tools in any quality improvement effort, along with the order in which they must be applied.

Every improvement project must start with a *project charter*. This is a living document in which the details of the project are established. Topics such as project title, purpose, scope, goals, milestones, and required resources are agreed on by the person requesting the project and the person executing it. The charter must be updated as the project moves forward. Once the project is defined and the team is organized, the *data measurement* process must begin. Some of the tools that can be used at this time are gage R&R, process capability analysis, histograms, box plots, dot plots, Pareto diagrams, scatter plots, run charts, and others. What we are trying to accomplish in this part of the project is to gain some process understanding through the use of many graphical tools. Remember from Chapter 5 that each graphical tool has its specific objective.

As we progress through our process knowledge continuum, certain hypotheses are gradually developed. Graphical tools alone are not enough to prove those hypotheses; some sort of analytical evaluation must be performed. Hypothesis tests such as normality, equality of means, equality of medians, equality of variances, correlation between variables, and statistical significance of factors are appropriate at this stage. Just remember that most of these hypotheses are developed with already collected data. Because of that fact, the next logical step is to experiment in a systematic way. Recall from Chapter 10 that experimentation is sequential; do not expect to solve all your issues with a single experiment. Be prepared to develop and perform many experimental designs to achieve a better understanding of the process.

And remember, throughout the project (not only at the end of it), monitor your process with graphical tools such as the control chart. Realize that control charts are not only used to decide when to stop your process and take some action; control charts are the heart of any continuous quality improvement endeavor.

12.3 PROACTIVE OR REACTIVE?

As mentioned earlier, if we want to continuously improve our processes, we need to change one of the biggest paradigms we face every day: "If it's not broken, don't fix it." Oftentimes, people do not react until it is too late. As established in section 3.1, we need to stop thinking that as long as our process is within the specification limits, nothing has to be done. Let me illustrate this concept with an example:

> A company is gathering data for the annual product review, or management review, to determine whether changes have to be made to its process controls. One of the key process variables the company measures is tablet hardness. The specification for that variable ranges from 4.0 to 11.0 kp. A control chart is developed in order to understand how that key process variable performed during the previous year. Figure 12.1 shows the individuals control chart for tablet hardness.

The argument presented in Figure 12.1 is the following: Should we take action on those points outside of the control limits? Some people might say yes, while some people might say no. Those people that say some action must

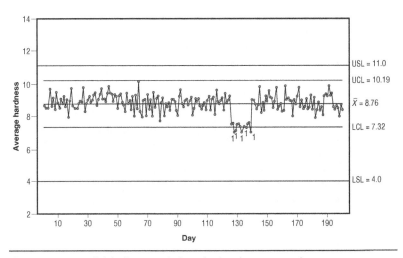

Figure 12.1   Individuals control chart for hardness example.

be taken will probably do so based on what we discussed in Chapter 11. Whenever a data point is outside of the control limits (or the chart is exhibiting a nonrandom pattern), that situation is being generated by an assignable, or special, cause. As mentioned, a special cause is something that must be investigated because it is not the inherent variation of the process (common cause) that is acting on the process but a situation caused by some external factor. However, there will be other people who might say that because the process is still within the specification limits, nothing has to be done yet.

The situation presented above clearly demonstrates the difference between two ways of thinking: *proactive* and *reactive*. As mentioned, if we want to continuously monitor and improve our processes, we need to switch from a reactive mode to a proactive mode. Before going further, let us see what the quality standards and regulations establish on this topic. For instance, section 9.1.3 (Analysis and evaluation) of the ISO 9001:2015 standard establishes that organizations shall analyze and evaluate appropriate data and information arising from monitoring and measurement. The results of analysis shall be used to evaluate:

a) Conformity of products and services
b) The degree of customer satisfaction
c) The performance and effectiveness of the quality management system
d) If planning has been implemented effectively
e) The effectiveness of actions taken to address risks and opportunities
f) The performance of external providers
g) The need for improvements to the quality management system[1]

Another example of process monitoring and improvement is found in the regulation related to medical devices, which states that:

> (a) Each manufacturer shall establish and maintain procedures for implementing *corrective* and *preventive* action. The procedures shall include requirements for:
>
> (1) Analyzing processes, work operations, concessions, quality audit reports, quality records, service records, complaints, returned product, and other sources of quality data to identify *existing and potential* causes of nonconforming product, or other quality problems. Appropriate statistical methodology shall be employed where necessary to detect recurring quality problems.[2]

It can be noted that the medical device regulation explicitly mentions the need for corrective and *preventive* actions. Furthermore, it mentions the need to identify existing and *potential* causes of nonconforming product.

So, if we take a look at Figure 12.1, it is true that it is not showing an existing nonconformance because it is still within the specification limits. However, it shows a potential nonconformance that must be addressed before it is too late. A reactive company would not do anything at this point, while a proactive company would investigate to find the cause of that potential nonconformance before a failure occurs. Which type of company is yours: reactive or proactive?

We have analyzed the regulation concerning medical devices. However, what happens in the finished pharmaceutical products arena? The regulation for finished pharmaceutical products establishes that:

> All drug product production and control records, including those for packaging and labeling, shall be reviewed and approved by the quality control unit to determine compliance with all established, approved written procedures before a batch is released or distributed. *Any unexplained discrepancy* (including a percentage of theoretical yield exceeding the maximum or minimum percentages established in master production and control records) or the failure of a batch or any of its components to meet any of its specifications *shall be thoroughly investigated*, whether or not the batch has already been distributed. The investigation shall extend to other batches of the same drug product and other drug products that may have been associated with the specific failure or discrepancy. A written record of the investigation shall be made and shall include the conclusions and follow-up.[3]

It is clear that the regulation on finished pharmaceutical products establishes that "any unexplained discrepancy must be thoroughly investigated." So, unless your company knows the causes for those out-of-control data points and has taken action to eliminate the possibility of those causes acting again in the process, an investigation must be enforced. A reactive company would not do anything at this point, while a proactive company would investigate to find the cause of that unexplained discrepancy before a failure occurs. Again, which type of company is yours: reactive or proactive? In any case, what do we call the actions taken to avoid this pattern repeating again in the future: corrective actions or preventive actions? In essence, those would have to be called *preventive actions* because no failure has occurred yet. More information about the difference between corrective and preventive actions can be found in the *Handbook of Investigation and Effective CAPA Systems*, by José Rodríguez-Pérez.[4]

12.4 NEXT STEPS

Now that I have stressed the importance of being proactive instead of reactive, it is time to begin our journey through the quality improvement of our processes. I hope this book has fulfilled your expectations. As mentioned in the Preface, my goal was not to teach an intensive course in statistics but to provide a how-to guide for the application of the diverse array of tools available to analyze and improve the processes in any organization. I hope that through your reading of this book you have obtained a better understanding of some of the available tools for monitoring and improving the processes in your organization. Finally, I encourage you to study, with a greater level of detail, each of the tools presented throughout the book.

NOTES

1. ISO 9001:2015, *Quality management systems—Requirements*, Sec. 9.1.3—Analysis and evaluation.
2. 21 CFR § 820.100—Corrective and preventive action.
3. 21 CFR § 211.192—Production record review.
4. José Rodríguez-Pérez, *Handbook of Investigation and Effective CAPA Systems* (Milwaukee: ASQ Quality Press, 2016), 8–12.

Appendix A
Variable and Attribute Data Applications

Many times, we are not certain which type of tool to apply for a specific situation. For example, we want to develop a control chart but do not know which one is the most appropriate for the type of data available. The same doubts could be generated when deciding which distribution to use for the analysis of data. Table A.1 shows a nonexhaustive list of some of the tools applicable to variable or attribute data.

Table A.1 Variable and attribute data applications.

	Variable data	Attribute data
Characteristics	Measurable Continuous	Counted Discrete Categories Binary
Examples	Temperature Length Time Speed	Number of defects Percent defective units Pass/fail Go/no-go
Control charts	$\bar{X}$ and R $\bar{X}$ and s IMR Median	p chart np chart c chart u chart

Table A.1 Variable and attribute data applications. (continued)

	Variable data	**Attribute data**
Distributions	Normal Exponential Weibull Lognormal	Poisson Binomial Hypergeometric
Sampling plans	ANSI/ASQ Z1.9	ANSI/ASQ Z1.4
Measurement instruments	Caliper Micrometer Scales	Plug gage Ring gage Pin gage

Appendix B

Applications for Various Graphical and Statistical Tools

Many times, we are faced with the following dilemma: We want to analyze some data but do not know which tool to use to analyze the data. I will split the discussion here into two topics: graphical tools and statistical tools. Tables B.1 and B.2 present a nonexhaustive list of the tools available for the kind of analysis we want to perform.

Table B.1 Applications for graphical tools.

If you want to . . .	Then you can use . . .	Find tool in section
Visualize the shape, central tendency, and dispersion of data	Histogram	5.2
Compare central tendency and dispersion of various groups	Box plot	5.3
Prioritize the order in which you deal with certain issues	Pareto diagram	5.5
Show the relationship between an independent variable and a dependent variable	Scatter plot	5.6
Identify the common and/or special causes in a process	Control chart	11.1
Determine whether data are random or exhibit some trend	Run chart	5.7

Table B.2   Applications for statistical tools.

If you want to . . .	Then you can use . . .	Find tool in section
Learn about the measures of central tendency, dispersion, and shape of the data	Descriptive statistics	4.4
Evaluate the normality of the data	Anderson-Darling normality test	5.8
Identify the variation caused by the process, by the measurement instrument, and by the analysts	Measurement systems analysis (gage R&R)	6.1
Compare the process variation against the specification limits	Process capability analysis	7.1
Compare an average to a single value	One-sample *t*-test	8.2.1
Compare the averages of two groups	Two-sample *t*-test	8.2.2
Compare the averages of two or more groups	ANOVA	8.2.3
Compare a median to a single value	One-sample sign test	8.3.1
Compare the medians of two groups	Two-sample Mann-Whitney test	8.3.2
Compare the medians of two or more groups	Kruskal-Wallis test	8.3.3
Compare the variances of two groups	*F*-test	8.4.1
Compare the variances of three groups	Bartlett test	8.4.2
Compare the variances of nonnormal data	Levene test	8.4.3

Table B.2   Applications for statistical tools.

If you want to . . .	Then you can use . . .	**Find tool in section**
Evaluate the relationship between an independent variable and a dependent variable	Simple linear regression	9.5
Evaluate the relationship between two or more independent variables and a dependent variable	Multiple linear regression	9.6
Identify the input variables that have an impact on the output variables	Design of experiments	10.1
Identify sources of process variation for variable data (subgroup size = 1)	IMR chart	11.5.1
Identify sources of process variation for variable data (subgroup size from 2 to 6)	$\bar{X}$ and R chart	11.5.2
Identify sources of process variation for variable data (subgroup size > 6)	$\bar{X}$ and s chart	11.5.3
Identify sources of variation for attribute data (percent defective)	p chart	11.6.1
Identify sources of variation for attribute data (number of defectives)	np chart	11.6.2
Identify sources of variation for attribute data (number of defects)	c chart	11.6.3
Identify sources of variation for attribute data (number of defects per unit)	u chart	11.6.4

Appendix C

Most Commonly Used Hypothesis Tests

At times, we do not know which hypothesis test to apply in a certain situation. Table C.1 shows the most commonly used hypothesis tests and how to interpret each one. The analysis will be based on an obtained p-value from any statistical software package.

Table C.1 Most commonly used hypothesis tests.

Test	Null and alternate hypothesis
General	H_0: Groups are not significantly different H_a: Groups are significantly different
Normality	H_0: Data fit the normal distribution H_a: Data do not fit the normal distribution
Randomness of data	H_0: Data are random H_a: Data are not random
Two-sample t-test	H_0: Means are not significantly different H_a: Means are significantly different
ANOVA test	H_0: Means are not significantly different H_a: At least one mean is significantly different
F-test	H_0: Variances are not significantly different H_a: Variances are significantly different
Regression	H_0: Data are not correlated H_a: Data are correlated
Design of experiments	H_0: Effect is not significant H_a: Effect is significant

Note: How to interpret this table:
- If the p-value $< \alpha$, reject H_0 and accept H_a.
- If the p-value $\geq \alpha$, there is no evidence to reject H_0.

Index

WHY ASQ?

ASQ is a global community of people passionate about quality, who use the tools,
their ideas and expertise to make our world work better. ASQ: The Global Voice of Quality.

FOR INDIVIDUALS

Advance your career to the next level of excellence.

ASQ offers you access to the tools, techniques and insights that can help distinguish
an ordinary career from an extraordinary one.

FOR ORGANIZATIONS

Your culture of quality begins here.

ASQ organizational membership provides the invaluable resources you need
to concentrate on product, service and experiential quality and continuous
improvement for powerful top-line and bottom-line results.

www.asq.org/why-asq

ASQ
The Global Voice of Quality

ASK A LIBRARIAN

Have questions? Looking for answers?
In need of information? Ask a librarian!

Customized research assistance from ASQ's research
librarian is one of the many benefits of membership.
ASQ's research librarian is available to answer
your research requests using the everexpanding
library of current and credible resources, including
journals, conference proceedings, case studies, and
Quality Press publications.

You can also contact the librarian to request permission
to reuse or reprint ASQ copyrighted material, such as
ASQ journal articles and Quality Press book excerpts.

**For more information or to submit a question,
visit asq.org/quality-resources/ask-a-librarian.**

ASQ

The Global Voice of Qua